# ATLAS *of*
# ENDANGERED
# SPECIES

MONDO

First published in North America by Mondo Publishing
980 Avenue of the Americas
New York, NY 10018

Copyright © 2006 Marshall Editions
A Marshall Edition
Conceived, edited, and designed by Marshall Editions
The Old Brewery, 6 Blundell Street, London N7 9BH, U.K.
www.quarto.com

ISBN: 1-59336-852-6
Library of Congress Cataloging-in-Publication Data
available on request.

Originated in Hong Kong by Modern Age
Printed and bound in China by SNP Leefung Printers Limited

Publisher: Richard Green
Commissioning editor: Claudia Martin
Art direction: Ivo Marloh
Design and editorial: Tall Tree Ltd.
Designers: Ed Simkins, Ben Ruocco, and Darren Jordan
Editors: Jon Richards and Catherine Saunders
Picture research: Lorna Ainger
Production: Nikki Ingram

The World Conservation Union is also known as the IUCN
(International Union for the Conservation of Nature and Natural
Resources). This organization was founded in October 1948 and it is
the world's largest and most important conservation network. It is
probably best known for its work in monitoring the state of the
world's species through the IUCN Red List of Threatened Species.

Its aim is to influence, encourage, and assist governments and
organizations throughout the world to conserve nature and to
ensure that any use of natural resources is ecologically sustainable.

# ATLAS *of* ENDANGERED SPECIES

S. ALLY M. ORGAN

# Contents

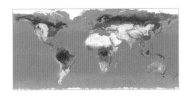

# CHAPTER FIVE: TEMPERATE GRASSLANDS

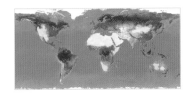

# CHAPTER SIX: DESERTS

# CHAPTER SEVEN: POLES AND MOUNTAINS

# CHAPTER EIGHT: OCEANS AND ISLANDS

# Introduction

Two hundred years ago, vast wilderness areas spanned the globe, largely untouched by humans. However, there has since been a population explosion, and today there are few areas left uninhabited or unaffected by people. Habitats such as tropical rain forests and grasslands are rapidly disappearing, along with the animals and plants that live within them.

## FACING EXTINCTION

At the time of writing, a staggering 15,589 species of plant and animal in the world are threatened with extinction, and 7,266 of these are animals. This figure includes one in four of the world's mammal species, one in eight of the birds, and one in three amphibians. It is likely that the true figure is much higher because only a fraction of the world's invertebrates have been discovered and studied. It is possible that some species became extinct before they were even discovered.

*Overfishing is just one of the ways that human activities are threatening the animals that live in the world's oceans.*

The giant panda is a much-loved animal, but it is facing extinction.

## THE RED LIST

*The Red List of Threatened Species* is published by the IUCN (International Union for the Conservation of Nature and Natural Resources). This conservation organization pulls together information on plants and animals from around the world and puts together a list of plant and animal species that it considers to be threatened. This list can be used to answer questions such as "How threatened is a particular species?", "How important is this species to conservation?", "What are the threats to a species?", and "How many threatened species occur in a given country?"

## THREATENED BY PEOPLE

An animal can become extinct for natural reasons. It is believed that a natural disaster wiped out the dinosaurs more than 65 million years ago. Scientists think that the earth was hit by a meteorite that changed the global climate and caused the dinosaurs to become extinct. Nowadays most extinctions are a result of the activities of people. Some 784 plant and animal species are now recorded as extinct, and a further 60 species are found only in captivity. The main causes of extinction are hunting, loss of habitat, and pollutants in the air and water. One of the greatest threats is climate change, which could affect the survival of all living species on Earth, including humans. However, conservation measures are making a difference, and several species have been brought back from the brink of extinction, including the southern white rhino, the black-footed ferret, the European otter, and the Christmas Island imperial pigeon. If people make an organized effort, the environment will see real benefits.

Every animal is placed in one of nine categories according to the degree of risk that they face. These categories are:

- **Extinct**
- **Extinct in the Wild**
- **Critically Endangered**
- **Endangered**
- **Vulnerable**
- **Near Threatened**
- **Least Concern**
- **Data Deficient**
- **Not Evaluated**

Those species listed as being Vulnerable, Endangered, and Critically Endangered are considered to be at risk of becoming extinct.

# Wetlands

Wetlands are among the most beautiful places on earth. They are incredibly diverse places—ponds, streams, rivers, lakes, swamps, estuaries, and mangrove swamps are just a few examples—and they support a range of wildlife.

•

Wetlands can be defined in many ways, but the Ramsar Convention, established to protect the world's wetlands, defines them as areas of marsh, fen, peatland, or water—either natural or artificial, permanent or temporary, with water that is static or flowing, fresh, brackish, or salt (including marine water)—that do not exceed a depth of 20 feet (6 meters) at low tide.

•

For a long time, wetlands were seen as wastelands that could be either drained for agriculture or built on. However, wetlands are not only important habitats for many species; they also play a major role in the water cycle. They regulate the flow of water and can protect towns and cities from flooding and tidal surges. They can even be used to clean up waste water at a fraction of the cost of state-of-the-art waste-water treatment plants.

# WETLAND WILDLIFE

The plants and animals found in wetland habitats have adapted well to the watery conditions they live in, which include fluctuating water levels and periods of flooding and drought. Many animals have developed unique features to enable them to exploit particular food sources. For example, most birds found in the wetlands have a particular shape of beak that helps them to extract food from mud or water more easily.

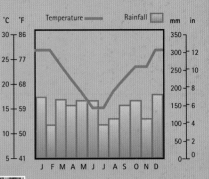

## Rainfall

In the Pantanal of South America, no month is dry. However, there are two main seasons—the "wet" season, which runs from December to March, and the "dry" season, which runs from April to November.

## Temperature

The temperatures rise steeply during the wet season and fall back down again during the dry season.

*Wetlands such as the Everglades in Florida attract a wide range of birds, many of which feed on amphibians and small reptiles. The abundance of wildlife attracts predators such as birds of prey and alligators.*

# DISAPPEARING WETLANDS

Almost 70 percent of people live along coasts, around lakes, and in river valleys. As a result, people have long tried to drain wetlands to control the flow of rivers and to extract water for drinking, farming, and industry. As much as half of the world's wetlands have been lost, mostly to agriculture. The wetlands continue to disappear, but people are beginning to realize their importance. Today there are conservation programs to protect what little remains of the world's wetlands.

*All forms of waste water, including sewage and industrial effluent, have been poured into wetland habitats.*

# Where Are Wetlands?

Unlike many other habitats, wetlands are not limited to specific regions or climatic factors, such as temperature, rainfall, or altitude. Wetlands can be found in some of the hottest places as well as the coolest, on plains and in mountains.

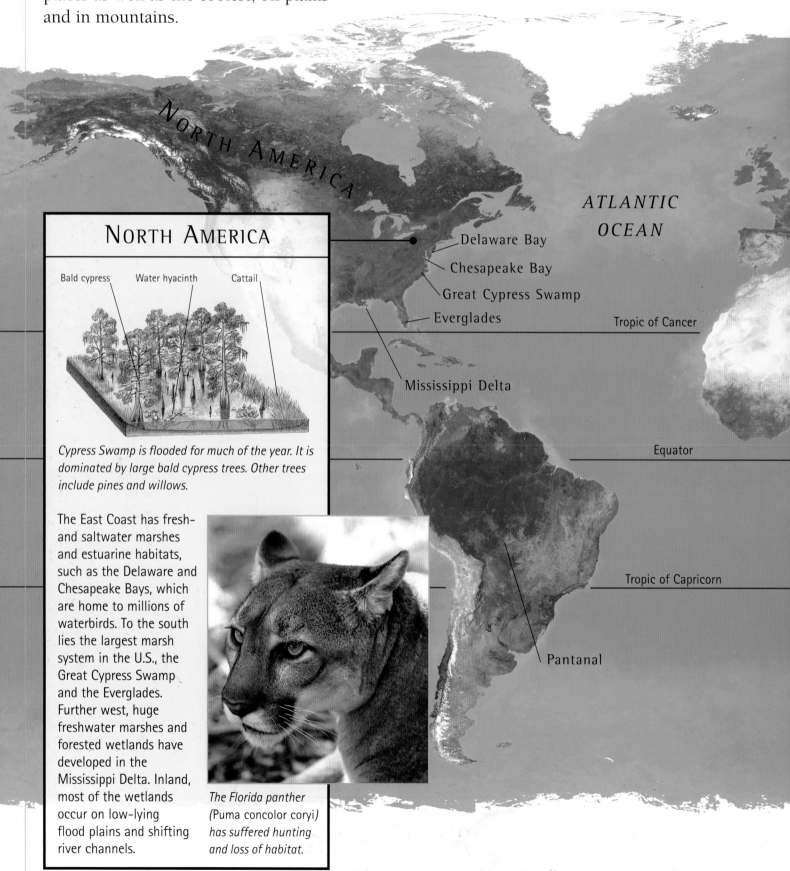

NORTH AMERICA

ATLANTIC OCEAN

Delaware Bay

Chesapeake Bay

Great Cypress Swamp

Everglades

Tropic of Cancer

Mississippi Delta

Equator

Tropic of Capricorn

Pantanal

## NORTH AMERICA

Bald cypress    Water hyacinth    Cattail

*Cypress Swamp is flooded for much of the year. It is dominated by large bald cypress trees. Other trees include pines and willows.*

The East Coast has fresh- and saltwater marshes and estuarine habitats, such as the Delaware and Chesapeake Bays, which are home to millions of waterbirds. To the south lies the largest marsh system in the U.S., the Great Cypress Swamp and the Everglades. Further west, huge freshwater marshes and forested wetlands have developed in the Mississippi Delta. Inland, most of the wetlands occur on low-lying flood plains and shifting river channels.

*The Florida panther (Puma concolor coryi) has suffered hunting and loss of habitat.*

# AFRICA

East Africa is dominated by the Great Rift Valley, Lake Victoria, and the Nile River. There are a variety of wetlands, including flood plains, swamps, and even lakes on the slopes of Mount Kilimanjaro. Lying on the northern edge of the Kalahari Desert, the Okavango Delta is the world's largest inland delta, and its wetland habitats are home to a vast range of animals.

*The Bangweulu Basin in Zambia is home to one of Africa's most important populations of shoebill storks (Balaeniceps rex).*

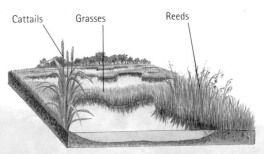

Cattails    Grasses    Reeds

*Wetlands have a range of habitats, from marshes to floodplain forests. The many waterbirds include jacanas, kingfishers, and fish eagles.*

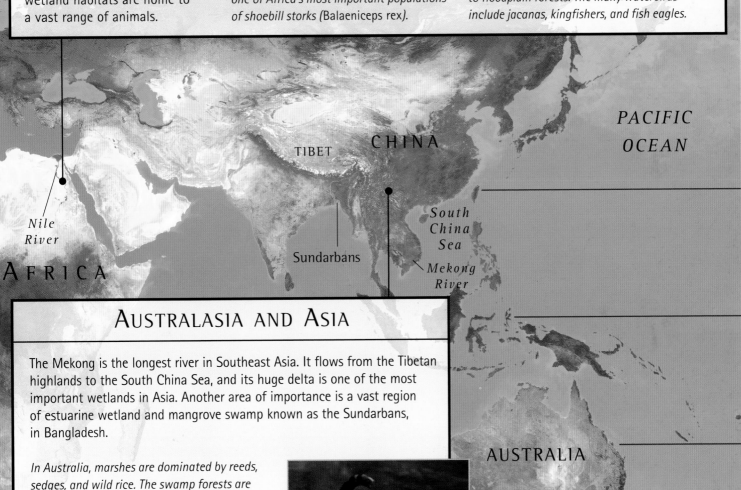

PACIFIC
OCEAN

CHINA

TIBET

*Nile
River*

South
China
Sea

Sundarbans

*Mekong
River*

AFRICA

AUSTRALIA

# AUSTRALASIA AND ASIA

The Mekong is the longest river in Southeast Asia. It flows from the Tibetan highlands to the South China Sea, and its huge delta is one of the most important wetlands in Asia. Another area of importance is a vast region of estuarine wetland and mangrove swamp known as the Sundarbans, in Bangladesh.

*In Australia, marshes are dominated by reeds, sedges, and wild rice. The swamp forests are dominated by river gums and paper-bark trees.*

Papyrus    Water hyacinth    Waterlilies and cabbages

*The Sundarbans are one of the last strongholds of the Bengal tiger (Panthera tigris).*

11

# North American Wetlands

When settlers first arrived on the shores of the Chesapeake Bay in 1607, it is estimated that there were almost 347,500 square miles (900,000 square kilometers) of wetland in the area that is now the United States. Today, less than half of that area remains, due to draining for farmland and development.

**Vast wetlands**

The vast North American wetlands include the length of the Mississippi River and the boggy swamplands of the Everglades in Florida.

## WEST INDIAN MANATEE

The West Indian manatees were once common in the Caribbean, northern South America, and along the coast of the southern United States. However, today they can only be found in a few locations around the Caribbean. Manatees feed on sea grass, which is declining as more and more silt is washed off the land. Silt makes the water cloudy and reduces the growth of the plants. Often manatees become entangled in fishing nets or get injured by the propellers of pleasure boats, especially in Florida. However, there are measures to protect them, such as warning signs to encourage people to drive boats slowly through manatee habitats. These rather comical-looking animals also have a slow reproduction rate, so their numbers take a long time to recover, even with protection.

# MAPPING THE WETLANDS

During the 1950s and 1960s, wetlands in the United States were being cleared at a frightening rate, and conservation groups were greatly concerned. Then, in 1975, the United States Fish and Wildlife Service set up the United States National Wetlands Inventory. The aim was to create detailed maps of wetland areas in every state. The first maps were produced in 1980, showing the location, shape, and characteristics of the wetlands. These maps have proved to be essential for providing information for drawing up conservation programs.

## ▲ Wood turtle

The wood turtle (*Clemmys insculpta*) lives on land and in water. It is found along forested rivers and streams. Its numbers are falling for a number of reasons. There has been an increase in small mammals that dig up its nests and eat its eggs. It also suffers from water pollution. In the past, it was collected for the pet trade, but this is now illegal. The best way to conserve this species is to control its predators.

## ▲ Spotted salamander

The spotted salamander (*Ambystoma maculatum*) is a large salamander that reaches lengths of up to 8 in (20 cm). These amphibians live in the eastern half of North America, in wetland areas that are surrounded by forest. They are threatened by loss of their habitat and water pollution.

## ▼ American alligator

In the past, the American alligator (*Alligator mississippiensis*) was hunted for its skin, and as a result, was wiped out over a large area. In the 1960s, it was on the brink of becoming extinct and was given protection. As soon as hunting stopped, its numbers began to increase. Today there are several million individuals, and some alligators are kept in special farms where they are raised for their skin. In some places, there are too many alligators, and they are either relocated or sold to alligator farms. Alligator hunting is also permitted in several states, although it is carefully controlled.

## ◄ Whooping crane

Whooping cranes (*Grus americana*) are large birds with mostly white feathers and red and black markings on the face and wing tips. Once they were found over much of North America, but by the 1940s, their numbers had declined to less than 20 as a result of the drainage of wetlands and shooting. However, a conservation program was set up, and now there is a population that breeds in the Wood Buffalo National Park, Canada, and spends the winter on the Gulf Coast. Today there are about 300 cranes living in the wild, plus some birds in captive breeding programs. However, cranes are still at risk from development, oil spills in the Gulf of Mexico, and collisions with powerlines.

## ▼ Paddlefish

The paddlefish (*Polyodon spathula*) gets its name from its extra-long jaw. This freshwater fish was once common in most rivers in central North America. However, its population is much reduced as too many have been fished, and the building of locks and dams on the rivers has interfered with its movements. There is also a new concern—as the numbers of sturgeon fall, its relative, the paddlefish, is fished for its eggs, which are sold as caviar.

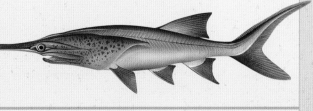

# South American Wetlands

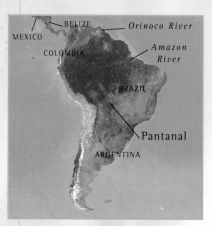

The Amazon Basin is a massive area of wetland covering much of the northern half of South America. Many rivers flow across the basin and unite to form the Amazon River. There are vast floodplain forests, swamps, and lagoons, and in the estuary of the Amazon River, there are expanses of tidal mud flats and mangrove swamps. There is also a complex of wetland habitats along the northern coast.

**Amazon wetlands**

The wetlands of South America are dominated by the mighty Amazon River, which flows across the continent, and the huge Pantanal swamps in the south. The Amazon River carries more than one-sixth of all the fresh water carried in the world's rivers.

## THE SPECTACLED CAIMAN

The spectacled caiman (*Caiman crocodilus*) gets its name from the ridge on its head between its eyes, which gives it the appearance of wearing a pair of spectacles. It is found in wetlands and along river banks from southern Mexico to northern Argentina. It feeds on insects, crabs, and fish. The caiman has long been hunted by indigenous people for meat, but they only took what they needed. However, since the 1950s, people have hunted it for its skin, and the population has fallen. Young caimans are also collected and sold as pets. Fortunately, the spectacled caiman has become protected, and its numbers are steady and even increasing in some areas.

# UNDER PRESSURE

The plight of the Amazon rain forest is well known, but the river and its vast floodplains are in fact the most fragile part of the Amazon Basin. Fishing is a major activity. Once it was just traditional fishermen providing food for the 100,000 people who live along the river, but now commercial fishing boats have moved in, and the fish catch is declining. Deforestation has resulted in soil being carried into the rivers, which makes the water cloudy and harms plants and fish. In some areas, gold mining has polluted local rivers with toxic levels of mercury. Now there are plans to build as many as 80 dams along the length of the Amazon River, which will have major consequences on the wetland wildlife.

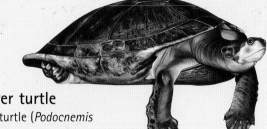

## ► Arrau river turtle

The Arrau river turtle (*Podocnemis expansa*) is a large plant-eating species of turtle weighing more than 100 lbs (45 kg). The females gather together and lay their eggs on sandbanks that are only exposed during the dry season. Unfortunately, these nesting sites are uncommon, and many have been damaged by the activities of people. This species has suffered from excessive collection of eggs and from hunting by people, so it is now protected.

## ▲ Boto

The boto (*Inia geoffrensis*) is a pink river dolphin with a long, plump body, and an extremely long jaw. It is found along the Amazon and Orinoco Rivers. During the wet season, it is agile enough to swim through the flooded forests searching for fish and crabs. The boto is threatened by entanglement in fishing nets, the building of dams, and collision with motorized boats, but it is protected.

## ▼ Central American river turtle

The Central American river turtle (*Dermatemys mawii*) lives in fast-flowing rivers. Most of the remaining turtles can be found in Belize and the Yucatan Peninsula of Mexico. Several hundred years ago, European settlers arrived in the region and hunted the turtles for their meat. Since then, there has been a steady decline in the turtle's numbers. It is still hunted because the species is not protected.

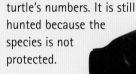

## ▼ Northern screamer

The northern screamer, or black-necked screamer (*Chauna chavaria*), is a ducklike bird that is found in a small area of northern South America, in northern Colombia, and northwest Venezuela. It lives in swamps and along the banks of slow-moving rivers. This bird has suffered from loss of habitat due to wetlands being drained for cattle and crops, its eggs have been collected, and there has been some illegal hunting. Its population is estimated to be between 3,000 and 5,000.

## ► Fluminense swallowtail butterfly

The fluminense swallowtail (*Parides ascanius*) is a large and colorful butterfly. It is threatened by the drainage and development of its swamp habitat near Rio de Janeiro, Brazil. Much of this has been caused by the expansion of the city. Now this butterfly is listed as being vulnerable, and only a few populations survive in a couple of protected reserves along the coast of southeast Brazil.

## ▼ Giant otter

The giant otter (*Pteronura brasiliensis*) is known as the river wolf because it is a fearsome predator. During the 1940s and 1950s, it was hunted for its valuable fur. Although trade in its fur is banned, considerable illegal hunting still takes place. The otter is also threatened by habitat loss, water pollution, and entanglement in fishing nets. Conservation measures include an education program to teach local people about the otter and schemes to encourage local people to benefit from ecotourism.

# African Wetlands

Africa has an extensive range of wetlands, from rivers such as the Nile, Congo, Niger, and Zambezi, to inland marshes such as the Okavango Delta—one of the world's most important wildlife habitats. In West Africa, the floodplains of the Senegal and Niger Rivers are found in the semi-arid region of the Sahel, where drought and famine are frequent.

## Water world

Despite its reputation as the driest continent, over four percent of Africa is covered in permanent swamps, and many other areas become swampy after heavy rain.

## THE AMPHIBIOUS ANTELOPE— THE SITATUNGA

The sitatunga (*Tragelaphus spekii*) is adapted to live in watery habitats. It is a good swimmer and can travel many miles in the water. It has long, splayed hooves that enable it to stand, and even walk, on floating islands of vegetation. These islands, formed from the matted roots of grasses, provide dry resting sites within swamps. However, on dry land, the sitatunga is clumsy and vulnerable to attack by predators such as lions and leopards. These antelope are suffering from loss of habitat due to the draining of wetlands. They are also hunted for their meat. The hunters use dogs to drive them into water, where they can be speared from a boat. Small numbers of sitatungas are found in swamp forests and marshes across central and western Africa.

# WATER OR WETLANDS?

Wetlands are an important source of water in Africa, particularly in the southern and central regions. Many countries face water shortages and are seeking new sources of water. This, combined with droughts in many parts of East and North Africa, is putting incredible pressure on wetlands such as the Okavango Delta, Lake Chad, and the Zambezi River. The increasing human population has resulted in extensive deforestation. The loss of forest is changing the water cycle and local weather patterns. Less water is evaporating from the leaves of trees, leading to lower rainfall in the area.

## ▲ Allen's swamp monkey

The Allen's swamp monkey (*Allenopithecus nigroviridis*) is found in the central Congo Basin and the eastern Congo. This monkey lives in swampy forests near rivers. It can swim well, and it dives to avoid danger. The monkeys live together in groups of up to 40 animals, communicating with each other using calls, gestures, and touch. Its numbers have declined due to habitat loss and hunting for meat. The monkey is listed as near threatened.

## ▶ Nile crocodile

The Nile crocodile (*Crocodylus niloticus*) is found across the African continent. It can grow to 16.5 ft (5 m) or more in length. It is found along rivers and in wetland areas, but its numbers fell during the middle of the 20th century, mostly due to hunting for its skin. Once the species was given protection, its numbers soon recovered. Now there are large populations in countries in eastern and southern Africa. However, the population is still low in western and central Africa.

## ▼ Pygmy hippo

The pygmy hippopotamus (*Hexaprotodon liberiensis*) is a piglike animal that weighs between 350 and 550 lbs (160 to 250 kg). They are found in dense, swampy forests near rivers. Over recent decades, numbers have fallen dramatically, and now only a few thousand remain. The main cause has been deforestation, but these hippos are also hunted for their meat and for their teeth. They are found in West Africa, where political unrest in many countries has also hindered their survival, and it is thought that they may already be extinct in Nigeria. The species is listed as vulnerable. Pygmy hippos breed well in captivity, and there are just under 200 in zoos and private collections.

## ▼ Lechwe

There are three species of lechwe, whose coloration varies from bright chestnut to grayish brown. In all species, the male has thin, lyre-shaped horns. Lechwe have long, wide-spreading hooves, which make them perfectly adapted to an aquatic way of life. Unfortunately, this also means that they cannot run quickly over solid ground, which has made them easy prey for lions, cheetahs, hyenas, and hunting dogs as well as human hunters.

# Asian and Australasian Wetlands

In South and Southeast Asia, many of the inland wetlands are created by the major rivers that cross the region, including the Ganges, Irrawaddy, Mekong, and Yangtze. Mangrove swamps and mud flats are common along tropical coastlines. Freshwater swamp forests occur inland of mangrove swamps.

**Largest wetlands**
The major wetlands in this region include the Sundarbans in Bangladesh, the Mekong Delta, and the Yangtze River in China.

## MAN-EATERS

The estuarine crocodile (*Crocodylus porosus*) is the largest and most dangerous of the crocodiles. It will attack any mammal at the water's edge, including humans. This crocodile is widespread from Sri Lanka to northern Australia, and is found in the brackish (partly salty, partly fresh) water of estuaries, deltas, and mangroves. It also lives in freshwater swamps. Numbers fell during the 1950s and 1960s due to hunting with high-powered rifles from motorboats. Hundreds of thousands of animals were killed each year. The hunting continues, although is has been made illegal in many countries, while the export of skin is strictly controlled. However, the preferred skins come from crocodiles under 5 ft (1.5 m) in length, so young animals are targeted. This affects the long-term survival of populations, and the estuarine crocodile is still considered to be at risk throughout its range. The only places with stable populations are northern Australia and New Guinea.

# THE SUNDARBANS

The Sundarbans in Bangladesh make up the most extensive mangrove forests in the world. This vast area is found at the point where the Ganges, Brahmaputra, and Meghna Rivers come together, creating a wetland maze of rivers, creeks, and lagoons. The Sundarbans are an important source of wood and fish for local people. Although the forest is heavily used, the mangroves support a rich diversity of animals, especially reptiles, birds, and mammals. Each year, thousands of tourists visit the Sundarbans Tiger Reserve to see the Bengal tiger and other rare animals, such as rhesus macaques and spotted deer.

## ▲ Proboscis monkey

The characteristic feature of the proboscis monkey (*Nasalis larvatus*) is the long dangling nose of the males, which hangs over its mouth. This monkey is found in swampy rain forest along rivers, where it likes to gather in large numbers. Its population size has fallen in recent years due to extensive deforestation in Borneo. The monkey is also hunted for its meat.

## ▼ Batagur

The batagur (*Batagur baska*) is one of Asia's largest freshwater turtles, and it reaches up to 24 in (60 cm) in length. It lives in estuaries and in tidal sections of rivers from India and Bangladesh eastward to Thailand, Malaysia, and Indonesia. Numbers have decreased steeply over the last hundred years, in some countries by as much as nine percent. This is due to a loss of habitat and the excessive collection of both adults and eggs. As a result, this species is now listed as being critically endangered. Although the species is protected, many are still caught each year. The first captive breeding of batagurs has been achieved at the Bronx Zoo in New York, and it is hoped similar schemes in other zoos will ensure its survival.

## ▲ Mekong catfish

The Mekong giant catfish (*Pangasianodon gigas*) is truly a giant among fish. It grows to 8 ft (2.5 m) in length, weighs a massive 660 lbs (300 kg), and is as big as a bear! It is found in the Mekong River and its tributaries, in China, and mainland Southeast Asia. Only a handful of catfish have been caught in recent years, down from about 80 a year during the 1990s. It is possible that water pollution is killing these giant fish. Other threats come from overfishing, dam-building, and other engineering projects along the river. It is now listed as being critically endangered. It is likely that this catfish, the largest freshwater fish in the world, will be the first species living in the Mekong River to become extinct.

## ▼ White-eyed river martin

The white-eyed river martin (*Pseudochelidon sirintarae*) was only discovered in 1968, when conservationists working in Thailand came across a strange swallow among large numbers of other swallows. Over the next three years, a few more specimens were collected at the same site. However, it has not been seen since 1978, and very little is known about the species. Ornithologists are hopeful that one day it will be rediscovered.

## ▼ Otter civet

The otter civet (*Cynogale bennettii*) is a nocturnal animal that is rarely seen in the wild. It looks a bit like a sea otter, with a long body, webbed feet, and very long whiskers. It lives in the swamps of the Malay Peninsula and on the islands of Borneo and Sumatra. The main threats to its survival are loss of habitat and hunting.

# Tropical Rain Forests

Tropical rain forests are ancient habitats teeming with life. They are the richest natural environments on earth, but they are also among the most threatened.

•

High temperatures and heavy rainfall create conditions that allow plants and animals to flourish. The variety of life found in just a small area is amazing. For example, 2.3 sq miles (6 sq km) of forest could be home to 750 species of trees, 400 species of birds, 150 species of butterflies, 60 species of amphibians, and thousands of species of plants. In fact, more than half of the world's species can be found in rain forests, and this figure will probably rise as scientists learn more about these forests and discover new species.

•

Although rain forests are incredibly complex habitats, they are also very fragile. Tropical rain forests once formed a green belt around the Equator, broken only by seas and mountains. They covered as much as 20 percent of the earth's land area. But over the last 100 years, people have been clearing these forests: now they cover just 7 percent of the earth's land, and the figure will continue to fall.

# RAIN FOREST WILDLIFE

The abundance of sunlight in the tropics makes plants grow quickly and provide food for many different animals. The tall trees form a canopy that shelters the rest of the forest. Most rain forest animals live up in this canopy, while epiphytes (plants that grow on other plants) such as ferns grow on trunks and branches. The shade of the canopy makes the forest floor dark and damp. Here a completely different range of animals lives among the fallen leaves and fruit.

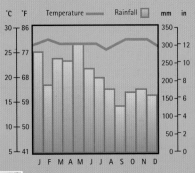

*This scene shows some of the animals and plants that can be found living in a rain forest canopy in Southeast Asia. Primates such as orangutans, gibbons, and monkeys use branches to move through the forest. Birds hunt for food and build their nests among the branches, while snakes, frogs, lizards, and other predators lie in wait.*

## Rainfall

The tropical rain forest is a very wet environment with rain falling almost every day. The total annual rainfall is between 60 and 98 in (1,500 and 2,500 mm). Certain months of the year have particularly heavy rainfall, while others have much less rain. However, the relative humidity is always high.

## Temperature

Temperatures are high all year, with only a few degrees difference between the warmest and the coolest months. During the day the temperatures reach 86–95°F (30–35°C), but they drop to 68–77°F (20–25°C) at night.

# DEFORESTATION

There are about 5 billion acres of tropical rain forests worldwide, but 35–40 million acres are lost each year. The major threats are logging for timber and clearance for agriculture and mining. The wood of the larger trees is in great demand, while growing populations in Africa, South America, and Southeast Asia mean that more farmland is needed. The practice of slash and burn clears large areas of forest, but the soil is poor. The land can only support crops for a few years, so farmers continually need to clear new plots.

*Farmers cut down, or slash, the largest trees for their timber and then burn the rest of the plants. This method of clearance is quick and easy.*

# Where Are Rain Forests?

The rain forests straddle the Equator, lying between the Tropic of Cancer in the north and the Tropic of Capricorn in the south. These are areas that are hot and wet for most of the year.

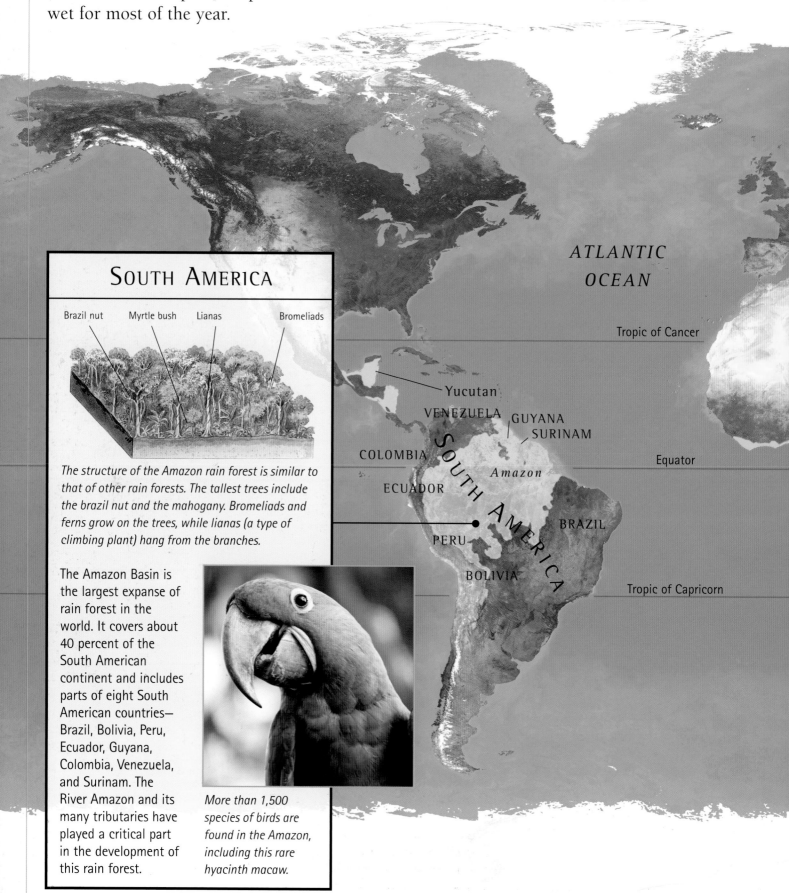

ATLANTIC OCEAN

Tropic of Cancer

Yucutan

VENEZUELA GUYANA SURINAM

COLOMBIA SOUTH AMERICA

ECUADOR *Amazon* Equator

PERU BRAZIL

BOLIVIA

Tropic of Capricorn

## SOUTH AMERICA

Brazil nut    Myrtle bush    Lianas    Bromeliads

*The structure of the Amazon rain forest is similar to that of other rain forests. The tallest trees include the brazil nut and the mahogany. Bromeliads and ferns grow on the trees, while lianas (a type of climbing plant) hang from the branches.*

The Amazon Basin is the largest expanse of rain forest in the world. It covers about 40 percent of the South American continent and includes parts of eight South American countries—Brazil, Bolivia, Peru, Ecuador, Guyana, Colombia, Venezuela, and Surinam. The River Amazon and its many tributaries have played a critical part in the development of this rain forest.

*More than 1,500 species of birds are found in the Amazon, including this rare hyacinth macaw.*

# AFRICA

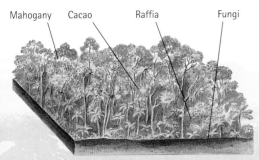

The largest trees in the African rain forest are the mahogany. Raffia palm and cacao grow beneath the canopy. Fungi are common on the forest floor, where they break down dead leaves and branches.

Most of the African rain forest lies in the Congo Basin, with a smaller area in West Africa and Madagascar. The Congo Basin is home to the second largest expanse of rain forest in the world. This forest is old but not as diverse as that of the Amazon. The island of Madagascar is home to many unique animals, in particular the lemur group, such as the aye-aye and the indri.

Pygmy hippos are found in West Africa. There are just a few thousand left and they are classed as being vulnerable.

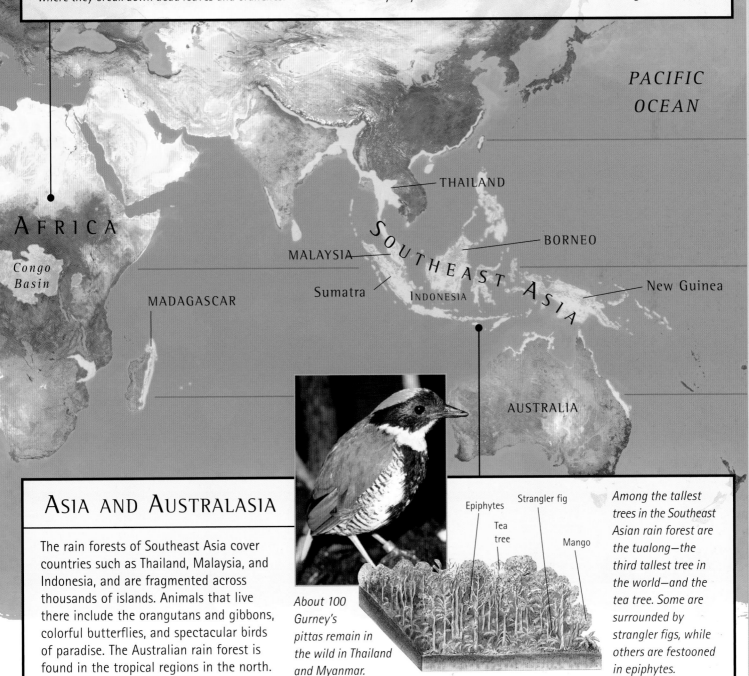

PACIFIC OCEAN

THAILAND

BORNEO

MALAYSIA

SOUTHEAST ASIA

AFRICA

Congo Basin

MADAGASCAR

Sumatra

INDONESIA

New Guinea

AUSTRALIA

# ASIA AND AUSTRALASIA

The rain forests of Southeast Asia cover countries such as Thailand, Malaysia, and Indonesia, and are fragmented across thousands of islands. Animals that live there include the orangutans and gibbons, colorful butterflies, and spectacular birds of paradise. The Australian rain forest is found in the tropical regions in the north.

About 100 Gurney's pittas remain in the wild in Thailand and Myanmar.

Epiphytes

Strangler fig

Tea tree

Mango

Among the tallest trees in the Southeast Asian rain forest are the tualong—the third tallest tree in the world—and the tea tree. Some are surrounded by strangler figs, while others are festooned in epiphytes.

# South American Rain Forest

**Disappearing rain forests**
There are rain forests throughout Central America, such as in Mexico's Yucatan peninsula, but the largest area lies in the basin of the Amazon River in South America.

The Amazon rain forest is the largest existing rain forest, and also the most diverse. Scientists believe that this forest could contain 90 percent of the world's species. However, more than one fifth of the Amazon rain forest has already been destroyed, and the forest that remains is threatened. The rain forests have been cleared in Central America as well.

## SYMBOL OF CONSERVATION

The golden lion tamarin (*Leontopithecus rosalia*) is a small monkey, weighing just 1lb (500g), that lives in the eastern rain forests of Brazil. About 30 years ago its numbers fell to around 200 due to the clearance of the rain forest, so some were bred in captivity. Recently some tamarins were re-introduced to the wild, and the population is now about 1,200. However, there is little chance for the wild population to grow as just 2 percent of their habitat remains. After an education campaign, the golden lion tamarin has become a national symbol of conservation in Brazil.

# Conserving the Amazon

The Amazon rain forest is being cleared at frightening speed. Between May 2003 and May 2004, an area the size of Israel was cut down. The way to slow this deforestation down is through sustainable management of the forest. This means using the forest in ways that allow people to earn a living from it but without damaging it for future generations: for example, by removing a few of the valuable trees but not cutting down the entire forest. Then, some of the cleared areas could be replanted in order to establish new rain forests for the future. However, the best way to conserve the most important areas is to create protected national parks and nature reserves.

## ▶ Bald-headed uakari

The odd-looking bald-headed uakari (*Cacajao calvus*) has a bright crimson face. There are four different subspecies with different colored coats, ranging from the pale orange and white coat of the white bald-headed uakari to the red coat and pale shoulders of the red bald-headed uakari. They are found in low-lying rain forest that floods. In areas of Peru and Brazil, these monkeys are killed for meat by hunters who travel through the flooded forests by canoe.

## ◀ Wooly spider monkey

The wooly spider (*Brachyteles arachnoides*) is the largest primate living in South America. It uses its long limbs and prehensile tail (which grips round branches) to move through the forest canopy. Like the golden lion tamarin, it lives in the rain forest of east Brazil, and due to habitat destruction and hunting, its numbers have fallen to below 1,000. A conservation program has been put in place, centered on the Serra dos Organos National Park in Brazil.

## ◀ Emperor tamarin

Emperor tamarins (*Saguinus imperator*) live in the southwest Amazon Basin, in east Peru and north Bolivia. They are small monkeys with mostly gray fur and a distinctive long, white droopy moustache. They live together in small groups of two to eight animals, led by the oldest female. This species has suffered from extensive loss of its rain forest habitat and is now classed as endangered in Brazil.

## ▶ Saffron toucanet

The saffron toucanet (*Baillonius bailloni*) is found in the rain forest of east and southeast Brazil, east Paraguay, and the extreme northeast of Argentina. It has olive and yellow plumage and a large beak to open nuts and fruits. It is rare in Paraguay and Argentina but still fairly common in the higher areas of the Brazilian forest. These birds are often hunted or captured and sold illegally as pets.

# African Rain Forest

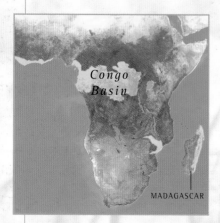

Congo Basin

MADAGASCAR

The African rain forests are home to an enormous range of animals. However, habitat destruction caused by logging, the demand for farmland, and the search for minerals and oil have resulted in many species being placed on the endangered list. In addition, the Congo Basin is disrupted by political unrest and civil war. Many people there live in poverty and have moved into the rain forests to search for food and fuel.

## Africa

The greatest area of rain forest lies in the Congo Basin in central Africa, but there are remnants of rain forest in West Africa, East Africa, and on the island of Madagascar.

## CHIMPANZEE

The chimpanzee (*Pan troglodytes*) may be one of our closest living relatives. An adult chimpanzee is just under 3 feet (1 meter) in height and weighs up to 132 lbs (60 kg). Its body is covered in black hair, and its arms are longer than its legs. Chimpanzees live in social groups of up to 120 individuals. They spend the day moving through the rain forest in search of food such as fruit, leaves, and occasionally birds, monkeys, and small antelope. One hundred years ago, there were two million chimpanzees in Africa. Today the number is just 150,000. Habitat loss, hunting for food, and poaching of young chimpanzees for the pet trade are the three major causes for the decline of chimpanzees in the wild.

# MADAGASCAR

The island of Madagascar lies off the east coast of Africa. Many Madagascan species evolved after the island split from mainland Africa 165 million years ago, and they aren't found anywhere else. Thick rain forest once covered most of the eastern part of the island, but factors such as a growing human population, high demand for wood as fuel, and a recent drought have resulted in much of the rain forest being cleared. Species such as the giant lemur and the aepyornis, or elephant bird, have already become extinct, and others are critically endangered. Conservation schemes have been set up to protect the remaining forest.

## ▲ Aye-aye

Aye-ayes (*Daubentonia madagascariensis*) are strange-looking lemurs with coarse, shaggy black or brown fur, tipped with white. They have large eyes, surrounded by black rings. Their ears are large and they have a long, slender middle finger with a long claw which they use for extracting insects from tree holes. The aye-aye is nocturnal and seldom seen. They were believed to be extinct until they were rediscovered in 1957. Aye-ayes are thought to be the most endangered of all the mammals living in Madagascar. Locals believe that they are a bad omen and often kill them.

## ▶ Olive colobus monkey

The olive colobus monkey (*Procolobus verus*) is a slim monkey with gray and orange fur. Its head has a crest of hair with whorls of hair on either side. The front and back limbs are similar in length. Unusually, the females carry their young in their mouth. These monkeys inhabit the rain forests of West Africa, which are under threat from deforestation and hunting.

## ▲ Fossa

The fossa (*Cryptoprocta ferox*) looks like a cross between a dog and a cat, but it is related to the mongoose. It is the largest predator in Madagascar and is found wherever there is rain forest. However, it is a rare animal whose population size is unknown. Fossas have no natural enemies, but local people kill them because they sometimes attack chickens. They are vulnerable because of loss of habitat and because they reproduce very slowly.

## ◀ Congo peafowl

Congo peafowl (*Afropavo congensis*) are secretive birds who live on the forest floor. They are slightly bigger than chickens. The males do not have the long train of feathers found on Asian peacocks, but they do have a head crest. Males are dark green in color with blue heads and chests. The Congo peafowl was discovered in the 1930s and they are found only in the Congo Basin.

## ▶ Ruffed lemur

The ruffed lemur (*Varecia variegata*) is only found in the eastern rain forests of Madagascar. It is threatened by deforestation, hunting and trapping for food, and the pet trade. The ruffed lemur depends on the larger fruit trees for survival, and these are often the first to be cut down when a forest is selectively cut. (This is when the more valuable trees are removed and the rest of the forest left intact.) Therefore, the ruffed lemur is one of the first species to disappear after selective logging.

## ◀ Indri

The indri (*Indri indri*) is the largest of the lemurs, with eye-catching black and white fur and long back legs. It is very agile and makes spectacular leaps from branch to branch. The indri is only found in Madagascar, where its numbers have fallen dramatically. It is severely threatened by the destruction of its rain forest habitat for fuel, logging, and farming. Local taboos, or ancient rules, mean that the indri is not hunted by local people.

# Southeast Asian and Australian Rain Forest

THAILAND
MALAYSIA
BORNEO
NEW GUINEA
INDONESIA
SUMATRA
AUSTRALIA

**Island forests**
Unlike the great expanses of rain forest in Africa and South America, the Southeast Asian rain forest is scattered over thousands of islands.

The Southeast Asian rain forest stretches from India to northern Australia. The rain forests in this region are among the oldest in the world, but their diversity is not as great as others. This region is experiencing a rapid increase in the human population combined with a massive growth in farming and industry. As a result, deforestation is happening everywhere, and the remaining forests are becoming even more fragmented.

## OLD MAN OF THE JUNGLE

The largest tree-living primate in the world is the orangutan (*Pongo pygmaeus*). Orangutans are solitary animals that can grow to 6½ feet (2 meters) in height. Female orangutans only give birth about every eight years, which makes them the slowest-breeding primates. Orangutans have long been hunted throughout the majority of their Southeast Asian range, as their size and slow movements make them easy targets for hunters. However, the greatest threat comes from loss of habitat. In the past 20 years, as much as 80 percent of their habitat has been lost to illegal logging, mining, and forest fires.

# DISAPPEARING RAIN FORESTS

The rain forests of Southeast Asia are under extreme threat from human activities. Indonesia and Malaysia are the world's largest producers of palm oil, and demand is increasing. Millions of acres of rain forest have already been cleared for growing palm oil trees. Illegal logging and gold mining are a problem too, especially in Borneo. Countries in Southeast Asia have established national parks, such as Khao Yai in Thailand, to protect particularly valuable rain forest or specific species. But long-term plans are needed, such as careful management of the remaining forests and encouraging consumers to buy timber from sustainable forests.

## ◀ Helmeted hornbill

The helmeted hornbill (*Buceros vigil*) is a very large bird that is found in the rain forests of Malaysia, Sumatra, and Borneo. Its distinguishing feature is a growth on the top of its beak called a casque which is made of "hornbill ivory." This ivory is highly valued for ornamental carving, and so these birds have been hunted for hundreds of years. Deforestation has also reduced the numbers of hornbills, as the birds need a large area of unspoilt rain forest in which to search for food, especially figs.

## ▶ Malayan tapir

The Malayan tapir (*Tapirus indicus*) is found in dense rain forest near water. It is a piglike animal weighing about 550–660 lbs (250–300 kg) with a short, flexible nose that it uses to find food. Its rounded, heavy body is ideal for pushing through thick undergrowth. Tapirs are nocturnal animals and travel long distances every night in search of food. Numbers have been reduced due to loss of habitat and hunting for meat.

## ▼ Tiger

Tigers (*Panthera tigris*) are solitary animals that need a large area of forest in which to hunt. As the forests have become more fragmented, tigers have come into greater contact with humans, who have killed them. They were originally hunted for their skin, but more recently, the greatest threat is poaching to supply tiger bone for some traditional "medicines." India has the most tigers—about 3,000—and they are given protection in 21 tiger reserves.

## ▶ Pileated gibbon

The long arms of the pileated gibbon (*Hylobates pileatus*) allow it to swing with ease from branch to branch. Pileated gibbons feed on leaves, fruit, and small animals. They are found in eastern Thailand, western Cambodia, and southwest Laos. As a result of deforestation and hunting, their numbers have dropped over the last 100 years from several million to fewer than 40,000.

## ▶ Sumatran rhino

The rarest rhinoceros in the world is the Sumatran rhino (*Dicerorhinus sumatrensis*). It lives in the rain forests of Indonesia and Malaysia, where its numbers have fallen by half over the last 15 years, mostly due to poaching for its valuable horn. Fewer than 300 survive in very small and scattered populations. It is closely related to the Javan rhino, which is also endangered. Fewer than 60 Javan rhino are thought to be left in the region.

## ▶ Queen Alexandra's birdwing

With a wingspan of 12 in (30 cm) or more, the Queen Alexandra's birdwing butterfly (*Ornithoptera alexandrae*) is the largest butterfly in the world and also one of the most endangered. It is found in the rain forests of New Guinea and local people collect them to sell to butterfly traders. As the numbers fall, conservation groups are helping to set up butterfly farms to save those in the wild.

# Temperate Forests

Temperate forests are found in a variety of climates. Most occur where the average annual temperature ranges between 37 and 64°F (3–18°C) with short summer droughts so the growing season is long.

•

There are three types of temperate forest. In the warm parts of the world, such as the Mediterranean, California, and South Africa, there are broad-leaved evergreen forests where the trees keep their leaves all year. In Europe and much of North America, the woods are dominated by broad-leaved deciduous trees, such as oak, beech, and ash, which lose their leaves in winter and form a thick canopy in summer. Further north the forests are dominated by coniferous trees, such as redwood, spruce, and pine, which have needles that can withstand extreme cold.

•

Once temperate forests covered the Northern Hemisphere, but over the centuries, trees have been cut down for timber and the land cleared for farming. Now only a fraction of the forests remain.

# DECIDUOUS FORESTS

Temperate deciduous forests, such as those in North America and Europe, have a layered structure. The trees grow to about 100 feet (30 m) tall. The canopy they form is open, allowing light to reach the ground. Birds, insects, and small mammals live in the canopy. There is also a lower layer of smaller trees and shrubs, as well as plants growing on the forest floor. Among the fallen leaves on the forest floor lives a wide range of animal life.

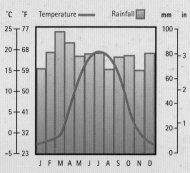

*This scene from a European temperate woodland shows the wide range of plants and animals that live in this ecosystem. Mammals include foxes, wild horses, and deer; birds such as woodpeckers make their homes in the trees; and a wide range of flowers and fungi lives in the shade of the forest floor.*

## Rainfall

Rainfall in most temperate forests is well suited to tree growth, and it is usually evenly spread through the year. However, the temperate evergreen forests experience drier summer months, and most rain falls in the winter.

## Temperature

A typical temperate deciduous forest experiences a warm summer, with temperatures reaching 68°F (20°C), and a cold winter, where they fall almost as low as the freezing point of 32°F (0°C).

## FOREST CLEARANCE

Over the last hundred years, the rapid growth of towns and cities has meant that more forest has been cleared for residential and industrial development and new roads. The forest has become fragmented, and animals have difficulty moving from one fragment to the next due to barriers such as housing developments and roads. In Asia there are considerable threats from the industrial growth of countries such as Russia, China, and India. However, in Europe and Australia, the decline has halted, and in some places the forest cover is increasing once again.

*Hardwood trees are slow growing, but their wood is in demand. Conifers are faster growing but produce a soft wood that has fewer uses.*

# Where Are Temperate Forests?

Most temperate forests are in the Northern Hemisphere. There are large expanses in America and smaller areas in western Europe, South Africa, and Australia.

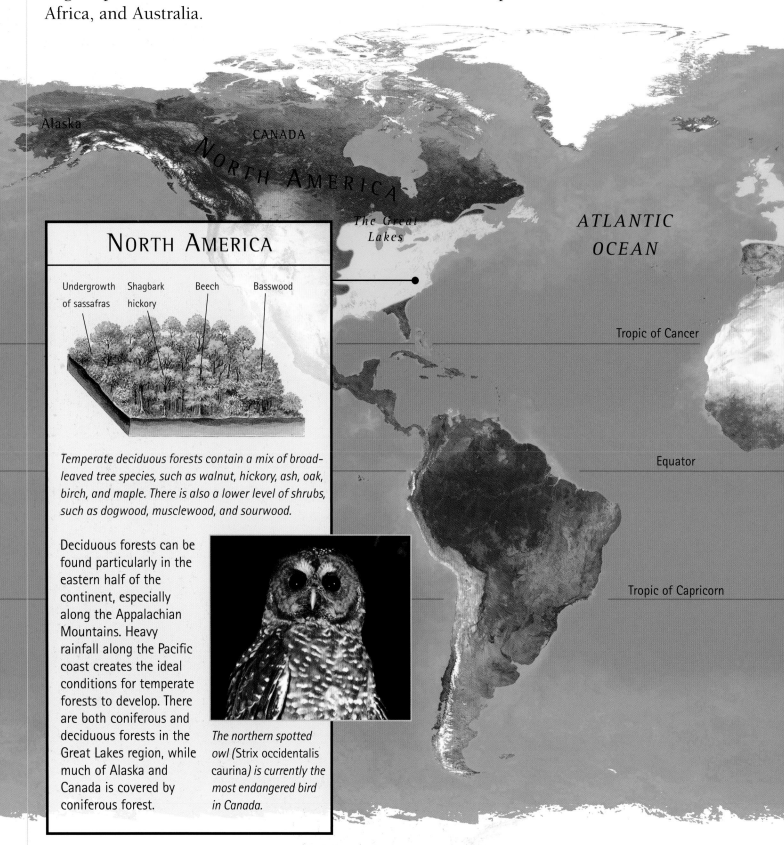

## NORTH AMERICA

Undergrowth of sassafras    Shagbark hickory    Beech    Basswood

*Temperate deciduous forests contain a mix of broad-leaved tree species, such as walnut, hickory, ash, oak, birch, and maple. There is also a lower level of shrubs, such as dogwood, musclewood, and sourwood.*

Deciduous forests can be found particularly in the eastern half of the continent, especially along the Appalachian Mountains. Heavy rainfall along the Pacific coast creates the ideal conditions for temperate forests to develop. There are both coniferous and deciduous forests in the Great Lakes region, while much of Alaska and Canada is covered by coniferous forest.

*The northern spotted owl (Strix occidentalis caurina) is currently the most endangered bird in Canada.*

Alaska

CANADA

NORTH AMERICA

The Great Lakes

ATLANTIC OCEAN

Tropic of Cancer

Equator

Tropic of Capricorn

# EUROPE

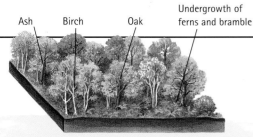

The largest trees in a European deciduous forest include oak, beech, and ash. Beneath these are shrubs such as hawthorn and hazel.

Most of the European temperate forests are deciduous, which lose their leaves in winter, making them look very bare. Further to the south, the forests are evergreen, with warmth-loving animals such as butterflies and lizards. Coniferous forests cover much of northern Europe and extend across Asia into Russia and China.

European brown bears (Ursus arctos arctos) are endangered by poaching.

RUSSIA

OPE

CHINA

JAPAN

PACIFIC OCEAN

INDIA

# ASIA AND AUSTRALASIA

Deciduous forests are found along China and Russia's Pacific coasts. Inland, bamboo forests are home to the giant panda. In Australia most forests are evergreen and dominated by the eucalyptus, the tallest broad-leaved tree in the world. The broad-leaved evergreen forests of Japan and Tasmania are dominated by trees such as the chinquapin and the southern beech.

The tall trees create an open canopy that allows other plants, such as tree ferns, to grow below.

AUSTRALIA

Tasmania

NEW ZEALAND

The endangered koala lives in eucalyptus trees and feeds on the leaves.

# North American Forests

North American forests are home to many large mammals, such as the grizzly and black bears, wolves, moose, and deer. Deciduous woodlands have the greatest variety of wildlife because the open nature of the canopy lets in sunlight, allowing more plants to live under the trees and feed more animals. Coniferous woodlands have a smaller range of wildlife because the needles of the trees are difficult to eat.

## Types of forest

Deciduous forests are found in the east, but temperate rain forest lies along the Pacific coast. Mixed forest is found around the Great Lakes, and coniferous forests stretch across Canada and Alaska.

## TIMBER WOLVES

Most wolves are found in remote regions of Alaska, Canada, and some of the central mountainous states such as Montana, Wisconsin, and Wyoming. The timber wolf or gray wolf (*Canus lupus*) is the largest member of the dog family, and it lives in packs. Packs hunt together, which allows wolves to kill large animals, such as bison, elk, and deer. The arrival of the European settlers marked the start of the decline of the wolf. Settlers hunted the bison and cleared the forests, pushing the wolves into more remote areas. Wolves were shot because the settlers feared them. As a result of education programs and legal protection, the number of wolves is now on the increase in some states.

# TEMPERATE RAIN FOREST

Temperate rain forests occur where west-facing mountains catch moist air blowing in from the sea, and where the temperatures are mild all year. The Pacific coast of northwest America is home to the world's largest temperate rain forest. The trees are mostly coniferous, and the trees, fallen logs, and the ground are covered with mosses and ferns. The mild, damp conditions are ideal for slugs, snails, and salamanders, while the fallen wood is food for many insects. Mammals roam the rain forest, and birds such as owls nest in the trees. However, the trees are in great demand for building timber.

## ◄ Bald eagle

In 1792 the bald eagle (*Haliaeetus leucocephalus*) was chosen as the national emblem of the United States because it is a species unique to North America. At the time, they were very common, with a population of between 300,000 and 500,000 birds. By the 1960s, the number had fallen to just 500 breeding pairs. The shooting of eagles, the use of poisons, spraying of pesticides such as DDT, the pollution of waterways, and the destruction of habitat have all contributed to the eagle's decline. The eagle is a protected species, and a massive conservation effort has managed to save the species from extinction. There are now about 60,000 eagles in the United States.

## ▶ White-tailed deer

The white-tailed deer (*Odocoileus virginianus*) lives in wooded areas in southern Canada and most of the United States, except for the southwest, Alaska, and Hawaii. When threatened, the deer raises its tail to flash the white underside as a warning to others in the herd. Nowadays white-tailed deer are extremely common and are the most numerous of the large North American mammals, with a population that could be as large as 15 million. However, one hundred years ago they were nearly extinct as a result of overhunting. They have benefited from the cutting of large trees, as this has allowed more shrubs to grow for the deer to eat.

## ▲ Grizzly bear

The grizzly bear (*Ursus arctos horribilis*) is a type of brown bear that is found in the forests and mountains of North America. It is a strong animal with a large shoulder hump and long claws that it uses to dig for roots. The bear gets its name from its grizzled coat, the brown hairs being lighter at the tips than at the base. Numbers of grizzly bears have fallen as a result of logging, mining, and the building of tourist resorts in the mountains. However, numbers are beginning to recover in areas such as Yellowstone National Park.

## ◄ Ivory woodpecker

The largest woodpecker in North America is the magnificent ivory-billed woodpecker (*Campephilus principali*). It inhabits mature swampy forests, known as bottomland swampy forests, where it searches for dead and dying trees infested with beetle larvae. Once these forests were found across the southern United States, but by the 1930s, most had been destroyed, and the birds were believed to have become extinct. However, in 2005, they were rediscovered in a remote nature reserve in Arkansas. The population is small but will hopefully continue to thrive.

# European Forests

**Range of forests**
Temperate deciduous forests are found in western Europe. Evergreen forests grow around the Mediterranean, and coniferous forests in northern and central Europe.

More than 5,000 years ago, much of western Europe was covered in temperate forest. However, over time, human activity has cleared much of this forest. Now just fragments remain, and much of this has been influenced by humans in some way: for example, it may have been managed, or cleared, and then allowed to regrow.

## SAVED!

The European bison, or wisent (*Bison bonasus*), is a large mammal covered in a shaggy, dark brown or black coat. European bison live in herds and both males and females have horns. The European bison was once found across Europe, but by the 15th century, hunting had wiped out most of the herds, and only a few survived in central Europe. It became extinct in the wild in 1925, but fortunately there were 54 animals in captivity. A breeding program was established to save the species from extinction, and since 1980, 24 herds have been re-introduced to the wild. Currently there are about 300 European bison living in the Bialowieska Forest in Poland. It has also been re-introduced to Belarus, Lithuania, Russia, and Ukraine.

# CONSERVING THE FORESTS

Western Europe is a densely populated region, so parts of the forests have been cleared for timber, farmland, mining, and developments. Further south, temperate evergreen forests have suffered too, due to forest fires during hot summers. However, recently there has been a move toward the sustainable production of timber, and funding has been given for planting broad-leaved trees. New forests are being established, including one in the U.K. Legislation is in place that protects forest habitats and species.

## ◀ Barn owl

The barn owl (*Tyto alba*) is rarely seen, as it is a nocturnal bird, hunting at night for small rodents, frogs, and insects. If food is scarce, it may be seen hunting by day. Typically it nests in tree holes and farm buildings. The decline of the barn owl started during the 19th century as a result of hunting. Since then, numbers have fallen, especially in northern Europe, due to the growth of farming, use of pesticides, and loss of nesting sites.

## ▶ Greater horseshoe bat

The greater horseshoe bat (*Rhinolophus ferrumequinum*) is named after the horseshoe-shaped nose "leaf" that is part of its echolocation system. These bats often roost in buildings during the summer and hibernate in caves, cellars, or disused mines during the winter months. The greater horseshoe is found in temperate woodlands of central and southern Europe, but its numbers have dropped greatly in northern Europe. The overall number of these bats has declined by more than 90 percent over the last 100 years, mostly due to the destruction of woods and roosting sites and the use of insecticides, which have reduced the abundance of the insects they eat.

## ▲ Spur-thighed tortoise

The spur-thighed tortoise (*Testudo graeca*) was once found in North Africa, southern Europe, and the Middle East, living in the dry temperate forests. Hundreds of thousands were collected over the years and sold around the world as pets. Many died because of unsuitable conditions and climate. The pet trade has been stopped, but now the tortoise is suffering from loss of habitat, caused in part by a high number of forest fires. Fires in southern Spain in 2004 are believed to have killed several thousand tortoises.

## ▼ Wild cat

The wild cat (*Felix sylvestris*) is often confused with the domestic cat. The markings are similar but the wild cat is a much larger animal. It feeds on small mammals and birds. Wild cats prefer to live in mixed broad-leaved forests, but habitat destruction has driven them into less suitable habitats, such as coniferous forests and hilly areas. The wild cat is found in Scotland and parts of central Europe. Habitat losses and hunting are the main factors in its decline.

## ◀ Hobby

The hobby (*Falco subbuteo*) is a fast-flying bird of prey with long wings. It hunts other birds, such as swifts, and large insects, especially dragonflies, which it catches in the air. It is a migratory species: those birds that spend the summer months in western Europe fly south to Africa for winter.

## ▶ Red kite

The red kite (*Milvus milvus*) is only found in Europe. It nests in woodland but searches for food over open land. It is mostly a scavenger, feeding on dead bodies of sheep, rabbits, and birds. Its numbers have fallen due to hunting, habitat loss, and egg-collecting.

# Asia and Australasia

Asian forests are suffering due to a growing population and an increase in industry. As China's economy booms, its natural resources are under threat, including the temperate forests, home to rare animals such as the giant panda. In Australia and New Zealand, the temperate forest has been cleared to supply timber for building and to make way for development.

**Forest locations**

Temperate forests are found along the coastal region of China and in Japan, New Zealand, and southern Australia.

## SIBERIAN TIGER

With a body length in excess of 10 feet (3 m) and weighing up to 750 lbs (340 kg), the Siberian or Amur tiger (*Panthera tigris*) is the largest and most powerful of the big cats. Increasing numbers of people and disturbances have driven the tigers out of northeast China and Korea into the forests of Russia. There are only about 330 to 370 adult tigers left in the wild, most of which live in the Sikhote-Alin mountain range. Here, threats come from hunting and poaching as well as logging and mining. However, ecotourism might save the tiger. The area could attract people wanting to experience the wonderful landscape and animals, helping to conserve the Siberian tiger.

# PROBLEMS WITH PREDATORS

Australia and New Zealand have been cut off from the rest of the world for millions of years. This has resulted in a unique range of animals, including the marsupials in Australia. However, the arrival of Europeans changed everything. The Europeans introduced animals such as dogs, cats, foxes, stoats, rabbits, and rats, which became predators of the native species. As a result, the populations of many native species have plummeted. There are other threats, too. Not only do the animals suffer from extensive habitat loss, but there have also been long-term droughts and huge forest fires.

## ▲ Numbat

The numbat (*Myrmecobius fasciatus*) is a small carnivorous marsupial from Australia that feeds on termites. Two hundred years ago, it was found in the southern semi-arid and arid areas and across much of the southern half of Western Australia. Now it is only found in the southwest of Western Australia. The numbat has suffered from being hunted by introduced mammals such as the red fox, and from the clearing of the land for farming.

## ▼ Giant panda

Today the giant panda (*Ailuropoda melanoleuca*) is found only in the mountains of western China, on the eastern edge of the Tibetan plateau, and in the provinces of Gansu, Shaanxi, and Sichuan. Its decline in numbers has been due to habitat loss caused by the pressures of a rapidly expanding human population. The bamboo forests have been cleared for farming, timber, and firewood.

## ◄ Kokako

The kokako (*Callaeas cinerea*) of New Zealand is a medium-sized wattlebird with blue-gray feathers and black legs and beak. There are two subspecies of kokako: the North Island kokako, with blue wattles under its throat, and the South Island kokako, with orange wattles. The South Island kokako is believed to be extinct. Over the last 20 years, the population of the North Island kokako has declined rapidly to about 1,200 birds due to deforestation and hunting by introduced animals such as rats and wild cats. Its survival depends on the control of predators. Some birds have been moved to nearby islands where there are no predators, and its numbers are increasing.

## ► Lumholtz's tree kangaroo

The Lumholtz's tree kangaroo (*Dendrolagus lumholtzi*) has a short stocky body with a long tail that it uses for balance. It is a nocturnal animal that moves among the treetops, rarely coming to the ground. During daylight it sleeps with its head between its legs, wedged in a tree. Tree kangaroos are endangered due to loss of habitat caused by logging.

## ► Bilby (rabbit bandicoot)

The bilby (*Macrotis lagotis*) is the largest of the small, rat-like marsupials called bandicoots. It has very large, hairless ears and long, slender back legs. One hundred years ago it was very common in southern Australia. Now there are just two small populations, in Western Australia and Queensland. Bilbies have suffered from hunting for their skin and from hunting as food by introduced foxes, cats, and rats. They have also suffered from lack of food due to long periods of drought.

# Tropical Grasslands

Tropical grasslands are huge, open plains with few trees. In the dry season, the ground is parched, but when the rains come, the landscape turns green. Tropical grasslands have different names all over the world—savannah in Africa, *llanos* and *campos* in South America, and rangelands in Australia.

•

Tropical grassland supports an unusually high number of large animals, both grazers (those that eat the leaves of trees) and browsers (those that eat grass), and their predators. The habitat is very productive—the soils are deep and fertile, and the grass survives grazing because the new growth occurs at the bottom of the leaf, allowing the leaves to regrow after being eaten. The plants of tropical grasslands are adapted to survive long periods of dry weather. For example, they have long tap roots, thick bark to survive fires, stems that can store water, and leaves that drop off to conserve water. There are few trees because it is too dry for most types of tree, and the grazing and browsing by animals and frequent fires prevent tree seedlings from growing.

# Tropical grassland wildlife

Grazing herbivores, such as impala and zebra, are numerous. These animals are adapted to eating grass. For example, ruminant mammals, such as antelope and buffalo, have a specially adapted stomach that contains a rumen. Inside the rumen are bacteria that can digest the grass easily. The herbivores attract predators, such as lions and leopards. There are also large numbers of scavengers, such as vultures.

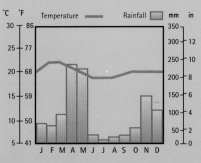

*The long grass of this South American grassland habitat attracts herds of grazing mammals as well as rheas (flightless birds). Termite mounds are common, and they attract anteaters.*

## Rainfall

There are alternating dry and wet seasons on the African savannah in Kenya. A small amount of rain falls in the dry season. The wet season is characterized by heavy storms in which most of the annual rain falls.

## Temperature

Tropical grasslands are warm all year, with average temperatures around 68°F (20°C). The temperature rises slightly during the wet season.

# Threats to grasslands

Overgrazing removes the protective cover of vegetation and leads to soil erosion. In addition, more grassland is being used for grazing livestock, such as sheep and goats. These animals are less adapted to surviving drought than the wild species, so people take water from rivers and waterholes to supply their animals, leaving less for the wild animals. An increasing human population also means that grasslands are being plowed up for development.

*Tropical grasslands have low rainfall, and some years have droughts. Although the grasses can grow back, many of the animals die. Droughts are more frequent as the climate changes.*

# Where Are Tropical Grasslands?

Tropical grasslands are found in those parts of the world that are warm all year round. They are located to the north and south of the tropical zones, for example, to the north and south of the Amazon and Congo Basins.

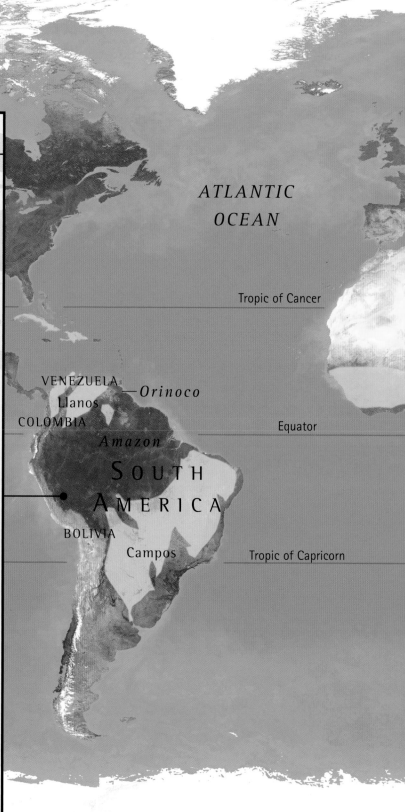

*ATLANTIC OCEAN*

Tropic of Cancer

VENEZUELA — *Orinoco*
Llanos
COLOMBIA

*Amazon*

Equator

S O U T H
A M E R I C A

BOLIVIA
Campos

Tropic of Capricorn

## SOUTH AMERICA

There are several areas of tropical grassland in South America, including the *llanos*, which is found in the Orinoco River Basin, the *campos*, which runs along the Parnaiba River to the edge of Pantanal, and the *cerrado*, a mixed habitat of woodland and grassland. The *llanos* of Venezuela, Colombia, and Bolivia floods each year.

*Typical* cerrado *vegetation grows on deep and well-drained soils. The dominant plant is the grass, but there are scattered trees that grow to between 17 and 23 ft (5–7 m). Animals include the giant anteater, armadillo, maned wolf, and pampas deer.*

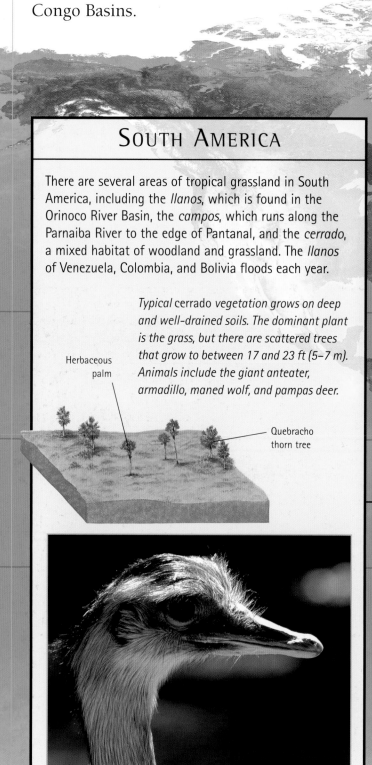

Herbaceous palm

Quebracho thorn tree

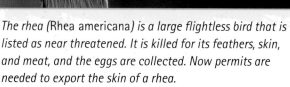

*The rhea (Rhea americana) is a large flightless bird that is listed as near threatened. It is killed for its feathers, skin, and meat, and the eggs are collected. Now permits are needed to export the skin of a rhea.*

42

# AFRICA

Tropical grasslands are found to the south of the Sahara Desert. They form a belt between the tropical rain forests of the Congo Basin and the semi-arid scrubland and desert. Tropical grassland once covered two-thirds of the African continent, but the area today is about half. In areas near the rain forests, there is also wooded grassland.

*The endangered African elephant (Loxodonta africana) is the world's largest land-living animal. Too many elephants in an area can cause problems because they damage the trees.*

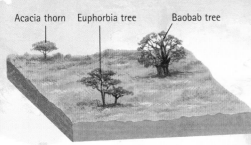

Acacia thorn  Euphorbia tree  Baobab tree

*The tropical grassland of East Africa is characterized by tall grasses that grow to 3.3 ft (1 m) or more in height, with trees such as baobab and acacia scattered over the land. Sometimes the trees form thickets. Large herds of grazing animals move around the grassland in their search for fresh grass and water.*

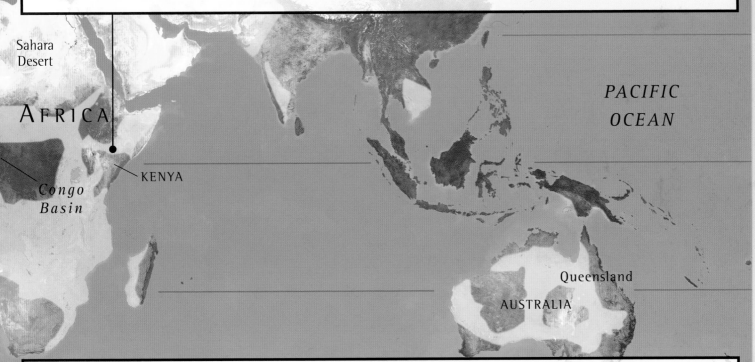

Sahara
Desert

AFRICA

*PACIFIC
OCEAN*

KENYA

*Congo
Basin*

Queensland

AUSTRALIA

# AUSTRALIA

The tropical grassland is found in a belt that stretches across the continent from Western Australia to Queensland in the northeast. As in other Australian habitats, marsupials are the dominant type of animal, and they include kangaroos, wallabies, possum, and bandicoots. These animals live in or near the scattered trees, which they use for shelter and food.

*The emu (Dromains novaehollandiae) is the largest bird in Australia, but its population is in decline through much of the region.*

*The Australian tropical grassland is an area of dense grass and scattered trees. The most common tree is the eucalyptus.*

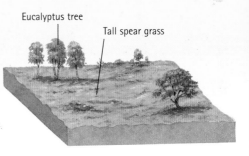

Eucalyptus tree

Tall spear grass

# African Savannah

**Wide savannah**
Savannah stretches across the continent and through eastern and southern Africa.

The African savannah is home to many herbivores (plant-eaters). More than 40 different hoofed mammals can be found on the savannah, many living in the same area. Some are browsers, which eat leaves of trees, and others are grazers, which eat grass. They can coexist in a small area because each has its own food preference, making it possible to live side by side with other species and not be in competition for food. For example, they browse at different heights, or graze different grasses, at different times of day or year. These herbivores provide a wide range of food for predators such as lions, leopards, cheetahs, jackals, and hyenas.

## WHITE RHINO

The white rhino (*Ceratotherium simum*) is a grazing mammal with a wide, square upper lip that is adapted for feeding on grasses. It has two horns, the front one being larger. Sadly, it is the value of its horn that has led to poaching. Today there are more than 11,000 white rhinos in Africa. There are two subspecies. The southern white rhino has increased from approximately 50 individuals in 1895 to more than 11,000 today. However, it is a very different story for the northern subspecies, which was once widespread. In 1960, there were an estimated 2,250 individuals. Poaching during the 1970s and 1980s devastated the northern white rhino, and by 1984, just 15 animals survived, all in the Garamba National Park in the Democratic Republic of Congo. They recovered slowly, but in 2003, armed poachers killed half the population. The survival of this subspecies is now in doubt.

# East African Problem

There are a number of large national parks and game reserves in East Africa, such as the Serengeti and Amboseli parks, which protect the savannah and its wildlife. However, this region has a fast-growing human population which requires more space, more food, and more water. Some people question why so much of the country is set aside for animals when people are living in poverty with too little food and water. Although the national parks attract tourists, little of this money benefits local people. Perhaps they might be more willing to protect their wildlife if they received some of the benefits of ecotourism.

## ▲ African lion

The magnificent African lion (*Panthera leo*) is fighting for survival. Lions are feared by people, and as a result, they have been shot whenever they have ventured onto farmland and come into contact with people. As the human population has increased, so has the conflict between lions and people. The loss of habitat and decreasing numbers of prey animals has forced the lion to hunt domestic livestock. Today the lion is protected in many countries, and only dangerous individuals can be shot. Now its survival depends on the cooperation of the local people. Fortunately, lions attract a lot of tourists, and if the lions disappear, the tourists will go, too. So there is a lot of incentive for people to conserve the "King of the Beasts."

## ▶ Bontebok

The bontebok (*Damaliscus dorcas*) was once considered to be the rarest antelope in the world, but careful conservation has ensured its survival in protected areas in South Africa. The Bontebok National Park in the Western Cape in South Africa was established in 1931 to keep the last few remaining bontebok from extinction.

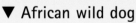

## ◀ Duiker

Duikers (*Cephalophus sp.*) are small antelopes. Their name is Africaans for "diver," due to their habit of bounding into the undergrowth when they are alarmed. They are shy nocturnal animals up to 28 in (70 cm) tall. There are two types of duiker: those that live in forests, and those that live in dense bush. There is only one species of bush duiker, which is the common or Grimm's duiker. This is the most widely distributed duiker in East Africa and is found in a large range of habitats, but never in deep forest. Its numbers have declined due to habitat loss.

## ▼ African wild dog

The African wild dog (*Lycaon pictus*) lives in packs of about 30. By hunting together, the dogs can bring down large prey, such as wildebeest. This species was once present throughout sub-Saharan Africa, but today it is restricted to fragmented populations mainly in southern and eastern Africa. They have been shot and snared by farmers and killed on roads. However, the current threat is disease. They are also in competition with other large predators, such as lions and hyenas. The population is less than 5,000, and they are listed as endangered.

## ▶ Grevy's zebra

There are two species of zebra—the Burchell's zebra (*Equus burchelli*) and the Grevy's zebra (*Equus grevyi*). The former is widespread, but the Grevy's zebra is under threat. It was found in Ethiopia, Somalia, and northern Kenya, but is currently restricted to northeastern Ethiopia and Kenya. Numbers fell during the 1970s, when its skin was a popular fashion item.

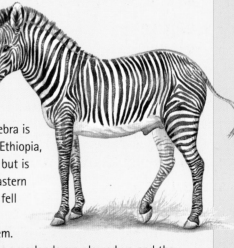

Now the species is suffering as grasslands are plowed up and they must compete with domestic livestock for grazing and water.

# South American Grassland

Llanos
Amazon Basin
PERU
BRAZIL
Cerrado
BOLIVIA
PARAGUAY
Andes
Campos
ARGENTINA

**Grassland areas**
The *llanos* lies to the north of the Amazon Basin. The *campos* and *cerrado* are found to the east and south of the Amazon.

South America has several areas of tropical grassland including the *llanos*, *cerrado*, and *campos*. Unlike tropical grasslands in Africa, very few animals live solely on these grasslands. Instead, they are found in a variety of habitats, including grassland. They move between the grassland and the surrounding mountains, rivers, deciduous woodland, and tropical rain forests.

## THE GIANT ANTEATER
The giant anteater (*Myrmecophaga tridactyla*) is a strange-looking animal. It has a very long, narrow head with an extra-long sticky tongue, and its body is covered in shaggy hair. Its legs are short with long, powerful claws. It is a specialist eater of ants and termites; it uses its long claws to rip open termite mounds ands its sticky tongue to pick up the termites. This animal is found in a variety of habitats, including grassland such as the *cerrado*, deciduous woodland, and even rain forest. It is under threat from loss of habitat due to expansion of farmland and from fires, both natural and those started by people. It is listed as being vulnerable.

# A BIOLOGICAL HOTSPOT

The *cerrado* is a vast area of tropical grassland and woodland in Brazil. It covers an area the size of Alaska—just under 800,000 square miles (2 million square km)—and represents about one-fifth of the land area of Brazil. One reason that this habitat is so important is its high biodiversity. It is described as a biological hotspot and, as such, is of international importance. However, the grasslands are under threat from the expansion of farming, especially for soybean growing, and coal mining.

## ◀ Chaco peccary

The chaco peccary (*Catagonus wagneri*) lives in dry grassland and thorn forest where there is low rainfall and high temperatures. Cacti grow in this habitat, and they are the preferred food of the peccary. The chaco peccary lives in small groups of adults and youngsters. It was first identified in 1975. Today it is found in western Paraguay, northern Argentina, and southeastern Bolivia. Its numbers are decreasing due to excessive hunting, cattle ranching on grassland, and general disturbance caused by road building.

## ▼ Giant armadillo

The giant armadillo (*Priodontes maximus*) has a tough shell of hinged plates that protects its body. It is found to the east of the Andes Mountains, from north Venezuela to north Argentina, living in undisturbed forests and grasslands. This animal has long been hunted for its meat, mostly by tribes who carefully controlled the numbers they killed. However, in the last 10 years, its numbers have halved as a result of increased hunting and loss of habitat. Fortunately, some of the larger populations survive in nature reserves.

## ▶ Maned wolf

The maned wolf (*Chrysocyon brachyurus*) is a foxlike animal with thin legs. It gets its name from the manelike strip of fur which stands erect when the animal senses danger. It is found in central South America, from northeastern Brazil to Paraguay and Peru, living in tall grassland and the scrub edges of forests. It is uncertain how many survive in the wild, but it is threatened by hunting and habitat loss. Farmers shoot it because it attacks domestic poultry. A number die on the roads, too. Until more is known about this species, it will be difficult to conserve it.

## ▼ Greater rhea

The greater rhea (*Rhea americana*) cannot fly and relies on its long legs to escape predators. Although they are found on grassland, rheas tend to avoid open areas and look for areas with tall vegetation, as their height allows them to see over the top of the vegetation and spot any predators. These birds have been killed for their feathers, which are used to make feather dusters, and for their skin, which is made into leather. They are also considered pests, as they will eat almost any crop. So as more grassland becomes farmland, more rheas are killed.

## ▶ Pampas deer

The pampas deer (*Ozotoceros bezoarticus*) is found on open grassland. This deer was once common on grasslands throughout eastern South America, but hunting changed that. It is estimated that more than 2 million skins of the pampas deer were exported from Argentina between 1860 and 1870. As a result, the pampas deer has been wiped out from most of its former range, and it is now considered endangered. There are some scattered populations, mostly in Argentina.

# Australian Grassland

Northern Territories
Queensland
Western Australia
South Australia

**Unique grasslands**
Most of the grassland is found to the north and south of the dry central region.

Australian tropical grasslands are home to many unique species of animals, including bilbies and wallabies. However, these are under threat due to the expansion of farmland and the introduction of pest species, such as rabbits, foxes, and cats.

## THE GREATER BILBY

The greater bilby (*Macrotis lagotis*) is a type of comical ratlike marsupial known as a bandicoot. It has oversized, hairless ears and long legs, rather like a kangaroo. These nocturnal animals are found on grasslands and in acacia scrub. Once, it was common across southern Australia, but now it is restricted to a few areas in Western Australia, the Northern Territories, and southwest Queensland. Its status is vulnerable. Its decline was mostly a result of excessive hunting for its skin, but bilbies are often inadvertently killed in rabbit traps or by poisoned bait. They are also hunted by foxes and cats, especially in times of drought. Fortunately, the bilby breeds well in captivity and some animals have been released back into the wild, for example, in Currawinya National Park in southwest Queensland.

# THREATS FROM WEEDS AND FIRES

Australian grassland is threatened in several ways. The expansion of farmland has meant more grassland is managed for livestock. There have been government programs to clear away scrub areas to create more pasture, and this has threatened the survival of several species. The World Wildlife Fund (Australia) is working with communities to stop this clearance. Other threats come from introduced plant species that have become weeds, such as the mimosa. These fast-growing plants out-compete native plant species and disrupt the habitat. In recent years, the exceptionally hot and dry summers have caused numerous fires, which race across grassland and woodland areas. Many of the plants are adapted to fire and can survive, but slow-moving animals cannot escape the flames, and those that do survive suffer from shortages of food afterward.

## ▲ Stick-nest rat

Once there were two species of stick-nest rats, the greater stick-nest (*Leporillus conditor*) and the lesser stick-nest rat (*Leporillus apicalis*). They lived in the semi-arid and arid grasslands of southern Australia and were named after their nests made of sticks. Their numbers fell due to competition from sheep and rabbits. Both species became extinct on the mainland during the 1930s, but some greater stick-nest rats survived on islands off the coast of South Australia. This species is listed as endangered, and there is a recovery program in place. The lesser stick-nest rat is extinct.

## ▼ Red kangaroo

The largest of the marsupials is the red kangaroo (*Macropus rufus*). This animal has long, powerful hind legs that it uses for hopping, and a long, heavy tail that it uses for balance. Its habitat is the open, arid grasslands and woodlands of central Australia. The kangaroos thrived when the first settlers arrived because they cleared forests and created grasslands. However, as kangaroos increased in number, they were seen as competing with sheep and cattle for grass. Large numbers were shot and used for meat and leather. As numbers started to fall, the Australian government brought in controls to maintain the population. Nowadays, commercially harvested kangaroos are used to produce high-quality leather, fur, and meat products, and most Australian states now sell kangaroo meat for human consumption. To make sure that the harvest is sustainable, each state is required to draw up a wildlife management plan.

## ▲ Bridled nailtail wallaby

The bridled nailtail wallaby (*Onychogalea fraenata*) gets its name from the white "bridle" line running down its neck and behind both forearms. During the 19th century, this wallaby was common, living in acacia scrub and semi-arid grassland. Then its numbers fell as a result of habitat loss, excessive shooting, droughts, fires, and predation by foxes, cats, and dingoes. By the 1960s, it was thought to be extinct. Fortunately, in 1973, a small population was discovered in a small area of central Queensland. Taunton National Park was established to protect the species. There is a captive-breeding program and plans to relocate some of the wallabies to other parks.

## ▼ Malleefowl

The malleefowl (*Leipoa ocellata*) is one of a group of birds called megapodes, which means "big feet." They are ground-dwelling birds, slightly larger than a domestic hen. They are only found in the arid and semi-arid grasslands of southern Australia. The malleefowl's numbers have fallen over the last hundred years, and now it is considered to be a threatened species. This has been due to habitat loss, frequent fires, and introduced predators such as foxes and cats.

# Temperate Grasslands

Vast expanses of grassland once covered much of the temperate regions of the world. These grasslands included the prairies of North America, the steppes of Europe and central Asia, and the pampas of South America.

•

The temperate grasslands lie farther from the equator than the tropical grasslands. Most of these cooler grasslands are found in the center of large continents where the winters are long, cold, and windy, while the summers are short and warm. This habitat is dominated by grasses, which have deep root systems and can survive fire and periods of drought. These roots help to build up a deep, nutrient-rich soil which makes the habitat very productive. The grasses produce most of their growth in spring and early summer. The roots survive the winter, and new shoots appear in spring.

•

The rich soil supports a large variety of plant and animal life, but it is also ideal for farming. As a result, much of the world's grasslands have been plowed up for crops. Now the North American prairie produces more wheat than any other area in the world.

# GRASSLAND WILDLIFE

The grassland is a patchwork of many different plant species. Some grow in the spring when there is plenty of water around, while others prefer the drier conditions of late summer. This habitat has very few trees. This is because trees are prevented from colonizing the grassland by fire, which spreads easily through dry grass, and by the constant grazing of animals. The grasses survive the grazing as their leaves grow from the base.

*Large grazers include deer, bison, saiga antelope, and pronghorns. There are insects too, such as grasshoppers and the caterpillars of butterfly and moth species. There are many burrowing animals that take shelter underground, including the prairie dog, burrowing owl, lizards, and snakes.*

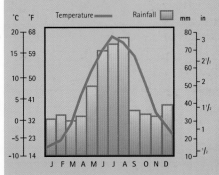

## Rainfall

In areas of temperate grassland, summers are fairly dry, and there may be periods of drought. The winters are wetter, with some precipitation falling as snow.

## Temperature

During the winter, temperatures fall well below freezing, 32°F (0°C), and there are hard frosts. In contrast, the summers are warm, with temperatures peaking around 70°F (20°C).

# DISAPPEARING GRASSLAND

The main threat to grassland wildlife is the continual loss of habitat to farming, both the growing of crops and grazing of livestock. In some parts of the world, very little remains of the original grasslands. This has pushed many species to the brink of extinction. Often the wildlife has to compete with herds of cattle for grazing. In addition, people have hunted animals such as deer and bison. Today there is the additional threat of climate change—the periods of summer drought are growing longer.

*Throughout the world, temperate grassland is making way for farmland, growing crops such as wheat.*

# Where Are Temperate Grasslands?

The largest areas of temperate grasslands are found in North America, South America, eastern Europe, and central and eastern Asia. There are smaller areas in South Africa.

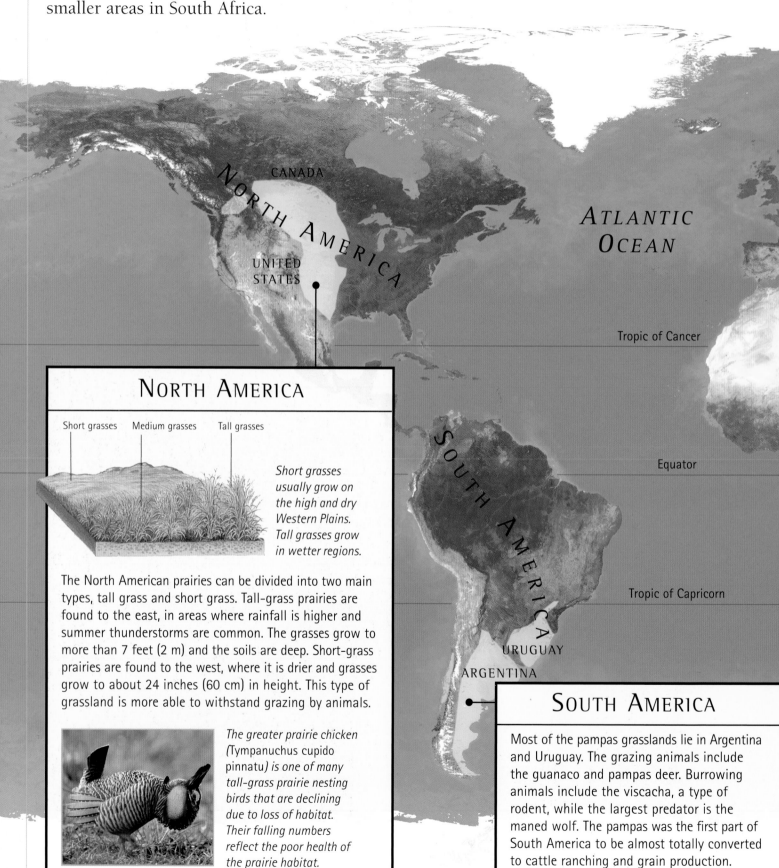

CANADA

NORTH AMERICA

UNITED STATES

ATLANTIC OCEAN

Tropic of Cancer

SOUTH AMERICA

Equator

Tropic of Capricorn

URUGUAY

ARGENTINA

## NORTH AMERICA

Short grasses    Medium grasses    Tall grasses

*Short grasses usually grow on the high and dry Western Plains. Tall grasses grow in wetter regions.*

The North American prairies can be divided into two main types, tall grass and short grass. Tall-grass prairies are found to the east, in areas where rainfall is higher and summer thunderstorms are common. The grasses grow to more than 7 feet (2 m) and the soils are deep. Short-grass prairies are found to the west, where it is drier and grasses grow to about 24 inches (60 cm) in height. This type of grassland is more able to withstand grazing by animals.

*The greater prairie chicken (Tympanuchus cupido pinnatu) is one of many tall-grass prairie nesting birds that are declining due to loss of habitat. Their falling numbers reflect the poor health of the prairie habitat.*

## SOUTH AMERICA

Most of the pampas grasslands lie in Argentina and Uruguay. The grazing animals include the guanaco and pampas deer. Burrowing animals include the viscacha, a type of rodent, while the largest predator is the maned wolf. The pampas was the first part of South America to be almost totally converted to cattle ranching and grain production.

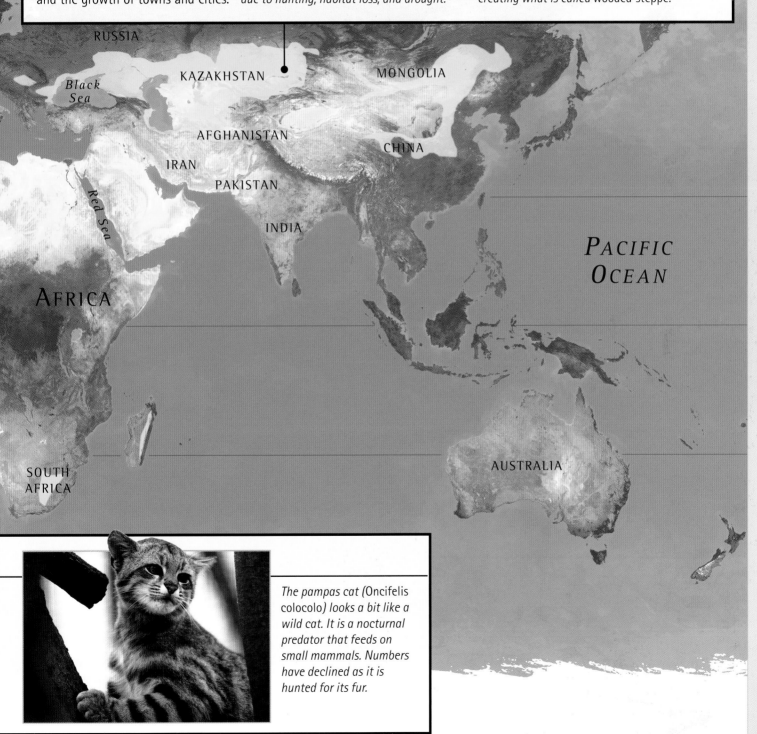

# EURASIA

The steppes stretch from eastern Europe through central Asia into China. Some of the land is arid, so the plants must adapt to the dry environment. There are herds of grazing antelope, gazelle, sheep, Asiatic wild ass, and horse, as well as many ground-nesting birds such as bustards. Although some of the more remote areas are unspoiled, much land has been lost to farming and the growth of towns and cities.

*Numbers of saiga (*Saiga tatarica*) have fallen by 80 percent in the last 10 years due to hunting, habitat loss, and drought.*

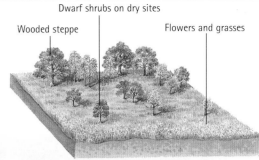

Dwarf shrubs on dry sites
Wooded steppe
Flowers and grasses

*Steppe is usually made up of short grasses. Trees grow where undulating ground retains water, creating what is called* wooded steppe.

RUSSIA

*Black Sea*

KAZAKHSTAN

MONGOLIA

AFGHANISTAN

IRAN

PAKISTAN

CHINA

*Red Sea*

INDIA

AFRICA

PACIFIC OCEAN

SOUTH AFRICA

AUSTRALIA

*The pampas cat (*Oncifelis colocolo*) looks a bit like a wild cat. It is a nocturnal predator that feeds on small mammals. Numbers have declined as it is hunted for its fur.*

# North American Prairies

**Vast prairie**
The prairies lie east of the Rocky Mountains, stretching from Canada, in the north, to Texas, in the south.

The North America prairies were once home to vast herds of migrating animals such as bison and pronghorn. As the herds moved across the prairie in search of fresh grazing, they were followed by predators, such as the wolf, coyote, swift fox, and burrowing animals such as prairie dogs and gophers.

## SAVING THE SWIFT FOX

The swift fox (*Vulpes velox*) is smaller, more slender, and lighter in color than the red fox. Once it was found in dry prairie habitat from southern Canada to Texas, but it began to decline more than 100 years ago. Swift foxes prefer open, short-grass and mixed-grass prairie, where they have good visibility and can move around easily. The swift fox has suffered from the conversion of prairie to farmland, as well as from hunting. In 1973 a captive-breeding program was established in Canada, and by 1997 just under 1,000 animals were released back into the wild in southern Canada. Similar schemes are operating in the United States, and numbers are increasing.

# FRAGMENTED PRAIRIES

The North American prairie once stretched from the Rocky Mountains eastward for more than 800 miles (1,300 km), and extended more than 3,000 miles (4,800 km) from north to south. Today it is one of the most endangered habitats, even more so than the rain forest. In some areas, up to 99 percent of the prairie has been destroyed in just the last 125–150 years. All that remains are a few fragments separated by expanses of cropland, roads, and developments. The animals that remain on these fragments are isolated from other populations, and this makes their conservation difficult. Conservation organizations are trying to re-create new prairie from abandoned farmland and to link the fragments by establishing wildlife corridors for animals to move from one fragment to the next.

## ▲ American bison

As many as 60 million American bison (*Bison bison*) once roamed the prairies. However, the arrival of European settlers led to the bison being hunted by the millions. For many settlers, killing bison was a sport, and they had competitions to see how many they could kill in a day. By 1890 fewer than 1,000 animals survived. The American Bison Society was formed in 1905 to save the bison. Some of the remaining animals were captured and bred in captivity. As their numbers increased, it was possible to reintroduce animals back into the wild. Now there are about 500,000 bison living on prairie grassland in Canada and the United States.

## ▼ Black-footed ferret

The most endangered mammal in North America is the black-footed ferret (*Mustela nigripes*). The species was once common throughout the Great Plains, from Alberta, Canada, to the southwestern United States, but became extinct in the wild in 1987. It lost its habitat as farmers plowed up the prairie. The ferrets prey on prairie dogs, so programs to exterminate prairie dogs from farmland also exterminated the ferret. A recent threat has been disease. In 1985 the last few black-footed ferrets were caught and bred in captivity. This proved to be successful, and ferrets have been reintroduced to areas where there are plenty of prairie dogs.

## ◄ Burrowing owl

The burrowing owl (*Athene cunicularia*) is a grayish-brown bird with long, slim legs and a short tail. It uses the abandoned burrows of prairie dogs and gophers to roost and to make its nest. It likes areas grazed by livestock since the grass is shorter and it can see farther. It also hunts for small mammals in areas where there is longer grass. As a result, it needs a variety of grassland habitats in order to survive. The burrowing owl is found in western North America—from southern Canada to Mexico. However, numbers throughout its range have fallen as a result of loss of habitat, and in many places it is now nonexistent or rare.

## ► Pronghorn

Before Europeans arrived in North America there were about 35 million pronghorns (*Antilocapra americana*) roaming the prairies. By 1920 fewer than 20,000 animals remained. Since that time, the pronghorn has been protected, and its numbers are thought to be up to about one million. This has been due to conservationists, government officials, and ranchers working together. For example, pronghorns do not jump over fences but crawl underneath, often getting tangled up and injured in the process. So, ranchers have placed special fence sections which allow the pronghorns to pass across with ease.

# Eurasian Steppes

The steppe of eastern Mongolia is one of the largest intact grazing ecosystems remaining on Earth. There are large herds of grazing Mongolian gazelles, whose annual migration is one of the greatest wildlife spectacles in Asia. The survival of this gazelle is important since its large numbers and pattern of movement influence the whole ecosystem.

**Vast grassland**
The enormous Eurasian steppes once stretched for thousands of miles from the Black Sea to the edges of the Pacific Ocean, but the region is shrinking.

## THE RAREST BIRD IN WESTERN ASIA

The Siberian white crane is an enormous white bird with black outer wing feathers and a bright red face. Hunting—especially in Afghanistan and Pakistan—and loss of habitat have reduced the numbers of this magnificent bird to less than 20, and it is on the brink of extinction. The crane is a migratory bird that spends the summer in northern Russia and flies south to overwinter in Iran and northern India. Prompt action is needed to save this species, providing that it is not already too late. There are some birds being bred in captivity. Experts recommend that some of the young should be released with the last of the wild cranes so that they can learn the migratory route. However, there is a further threat to cranes from the highly contagious avian flu, which could kill the remaining birds.

# CHANGING WAY OF LIFE

The Mongolian steppe is sparsely populated by nomadic herders who have had little impact on the environment. However, in recent years, some of these nomadic people have started to change their way of life—they are spending more time in one place, instead of moving to new grazing grounds, and this is causing overgrazing in some areas. There are other threats, too, including the building of roads and railroads, which create barriers, disrupting the migration of the gazelle. Agricultural expansion is leading to more fences and the introduction of herds of cattle and sheep that compete with the wildlife.

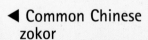

## ▲ Przewalski's horse

Przewalski's horse (*Equus ferus przewalskii*) became extinct in the wild at the end of the 1960s. It had been found on semi-arid and arid steppe grasslands in western Mongolia, northern China, and eastern Kazakhstan. The species was saved from complete extinction by a captive-breeding program. These horses bred well, and by 1999 there were 1,590 horses in captivity. The breeding program was carefully monitored to make sure the animals did not become too inbred. The horses are now gradually being reintroduced back into the wild.

## ◀ Common Chinese zokor

The common Chinese zokor (*Myospalax fontanieri*) is a ratlike rodent that feeds on roots. It digs underground storage chambers where it keeps plant foods. Zokors are often considered pests because they damage the roots of plants, so they are frequently killed. The bones of zokors are often used instead of tiger bones in some traditional Chinese medicines. While this has helped to save the tiger, numbers of the zokor are declining. Conservationists are trying to persuade landowners in western China to stop killing the animals.

## ▲ Onager

The onager is a subspecies of the Asiatic wild ass (*Equus hemionus*). All Asiatic wild asses are rare, and their distribution is much reduced. They were once found from the Red Sea to Mongolia. Today, the onager is found only in Iran and Turkmenistan, where they are critically endangered. Poaching for their meat and skin has been the main cause of their decline. The scattered populations are isolated from each other, and this is leading to inbreeding, which threatens the long-term health and survival of the animals.

## ▶ Great bustard

The great bustard (*Otis tarda*) is a large bird with a gray head and neck, and a brown back barred with black. Its range stretches across Europe and Asia, where it is found on grassland and steppe, in areas where there is little human disturbance. Its numbers have fallen as a result of habitat loss caused by the plowing of grasslands for farmland; irrigation schemes; the construction of roads, power lines, and fences; and the use of pesticides and chemical fertilizers. Conservation of the species involves the protection of breeding sites, traditional farming methods, fire prevention, banning of illegal hunting, and devising ways of preventing the bird colliding with power lines.

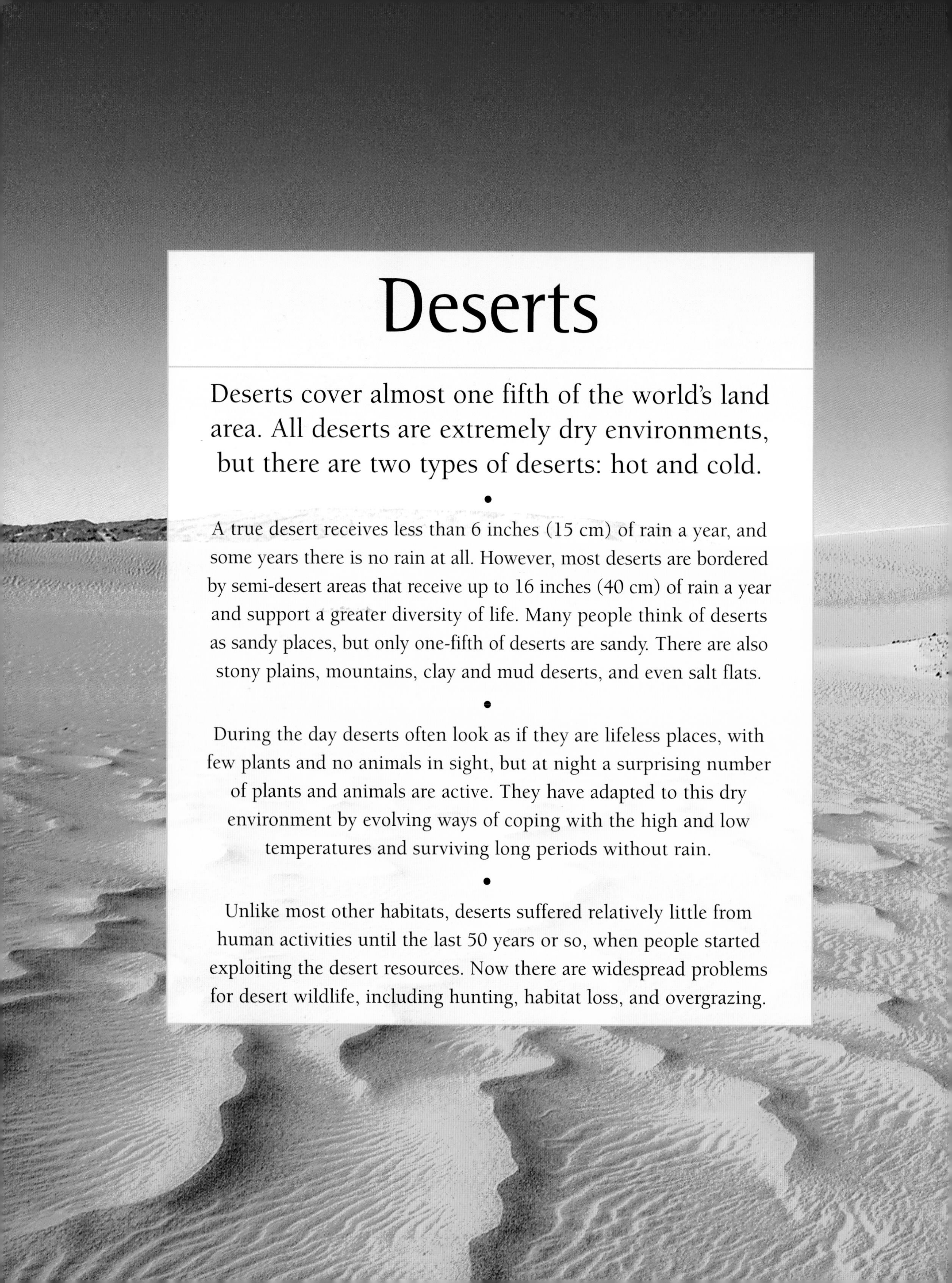

# Deserts

Deserts cover almost one fifth of the world's land area. All deserts are extremely dry environments, but there are two types of deserts: hot and cold.

•

A true desert receives less than 6 inches (15 cm) of rain a year, and some years there is no rain at all. However, most deserts are bordered by semi-desert areas that receive up to 16 inches (40 cm) of rain a year and support a greater diversity of life. Many people think of deserts as sandy places, but only one-fifth of deserts are sandy. There are also stony plains, mountains, clay and mud deserts, and even salt flats.

•

During the day deserts often look as if they are lifeless places, with few plants and no animals in sight, but at night a surprising number of plants and animals are active. They have adapted to this dry environment by evolving ways of coping with the high and low temperatures and surviving long periods without rain.

•

Unlike most other habitats, deserts suffered relatively little from human activities until the last 50 years or so, when people started exploiting the desert resources. Now there are widespread problems for desert wildlife, including hunting, habitat loss, and overgrazing.

# HOT DESERT WILDLIFE

In a hot desert, few animals come out during the burning heat of the day. They stay cool by sheltering in holes, in tunnels, or under bushes in the shade, and then emerge at night when it is cooler. Water is scarce in the desert, so animals either stay close to waterholes or have adapted so that they can survive on very little water. For example, the jerboa, a type of rodent, gains all the water it needs from its food.

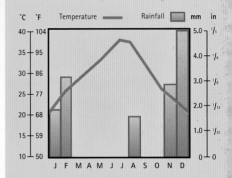

*Permanent waterholes, or oases, are lifelines in the desert. Here date palms provide food and shelter. Visitors to the water include dragonflies, birds, and mammals such as oryx. Vultures soar overhead looking for dead bodies on which they can feed.*

## Rainfall

Rainfall is low in a desert, and in some years there is no rain at all. The rain falls within a short period, often in heavy downpours.

## Temperature

In hot deserts day temperatures are high all year round. However, at night they fall considerably, often as low as freezing—32°F (0°C). In fact, the daily temperature range is greater than in any other habitat. Cold deserts, such as the Gobi Desert in Mongolia, are extremely cold in winter but scorching hot in summer.

# HUMAN ACTIVITIES

In areas such as the Middle East, the main threats to desert wildlife are hunting for sport, oil extraction, and pipeline construction. In Africa, central Asia, and parts of Australia, livestock graze in semi-desert areas. Overgrazing of goats and sheep removes the plant cover so the soil can be blown away by winds. In a short time, the ground is unable to support plant growth, and the land becomes desert. This is called desertification. However, few animals colonize these new desert areas.

*Damage from four-wheel-drive vehicles is on the increase in desert areas. Sandy deserts have a thin crusty layer over the surface, which stabilizes the sand. This is easily damaged by tires.*

# Where Are Deserts?

Most of the world's deserts can be found to the north and south of the equator in areas where there is high atmospheric pressure for much of the year. These conditions prevent winds from bringing in rain.

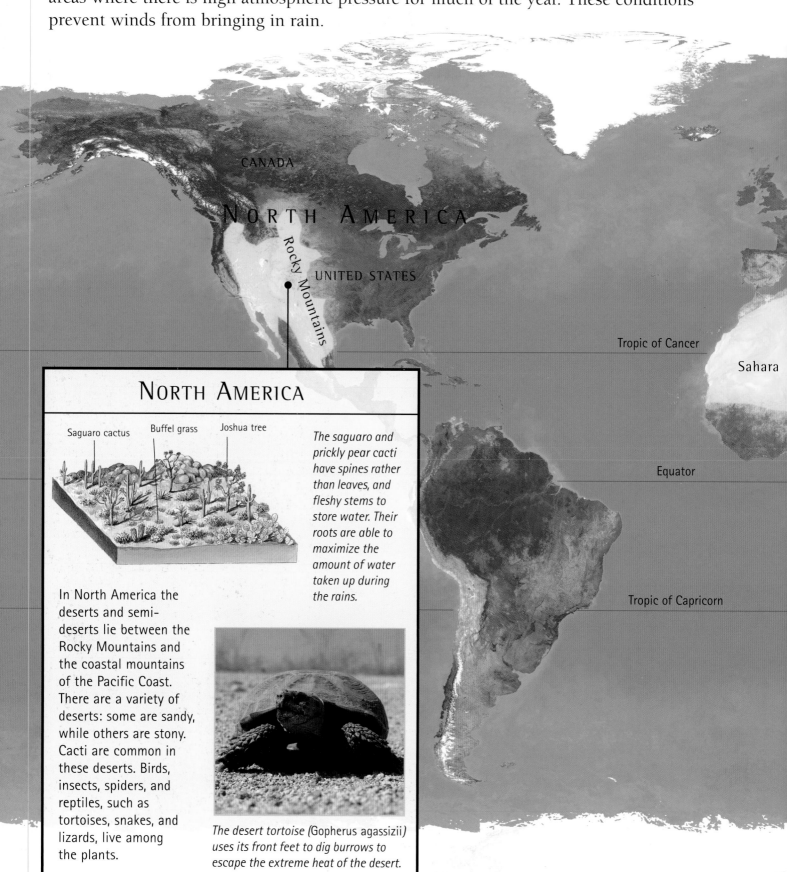

CANADA

NORTH AMERICA

Rocky Mountains

UNITED STATES

Tropic of Cancer

Sahara

Equator

Tropic of Capricorn

## NORTH AMERICA

Saguaro cactus    Buffel grass    Joshua tree

*The saguaro and prickly pear cacti have spines rather than leaves, and fleshy stems to store water. Their roots are able to maximize the amount of water taken up during the rains.*

In North America the deserts and semi-deserts lie between the Rocky Mountains and the coastal mountains of the Pacific Coast. There are a variety of deserts: some are sandy, while others are stony. Cacti are common in these deserts. Birds, insects, spiders, and reptiles, such as tortoises, snakes, and lizards, live among the plants.

*The desert tortoise (Gopherus agassizii) uses its front feet to dig burrows to escape the extreme heat of the desert.*

# AFRICA AND SOUTHWESTERN ASIA

The Sahara Desert in North Africa is the world's largest hot desert and covers an area of about 3,500,000 square miles (9,000,000 km²), making it nearly as big as the United States. To its south there is a belt of semi-desert and arid grassland. The world's driest and hottest desert is the Arabian Desert in the Middle East, east of the Red Sea.

*The last wild Arabian oryx (Oryx leucoryx) was shot in 1972, but the oryx was saved from extinction by captive-breeding programs.*

*In a sandy desert, few plants can take root on the shifting sand dunes, but drought-resistant plants can grow on gravel plains. Palm trees are found in areas where water collects during the rains.*

Date palms    Acacia bush    Oleander bush

MONGOLIA

• Gobi Desert

CHINA

Arabian Desert

Desert

Red Sea

AFRICA

Kalahari Desert

# ASIA AND AUSTRALIA

Much of central Asia is covered in cold deserts, which include the Turkestan Desert, Takla Makan Desert, and the Gobi Desert. Further south, there is a large area of hot desert in India and Pakistan. Hot desert covers much of western and central Australia.

Saxaul bushes    Sagebrush    Saltwort

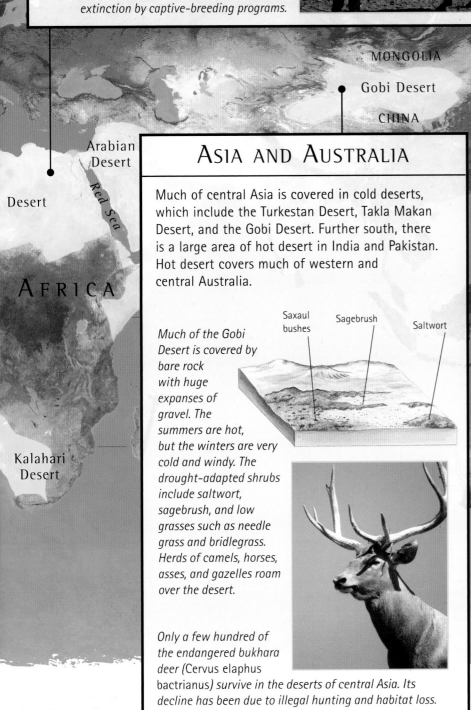

*Much of the Gobi Desert is covered by bare rock with huge expanses of gravel. The summers are hot, but the winters are very cold and windy. The drought-adapted shrubs include saltwort, sagebrush, and low grasses such as needle grass and bridlegrass. Herds of camels, horses, asses, and gazelles roam over the desert.*

*Only a few hundred of the endangered bukhara deer (Cervus elaphus bactrianus) survive in the deserts of central Asia. Its decline has been due to illegal hunting and habitat loss.*

AUSTRALIA

Great Sandy Desert    Simpson Desert

# African Deserts

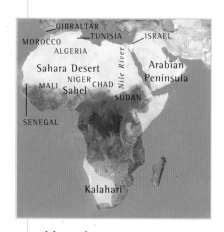

**Vast deserts**
Much of Africa is covered by desert, including the Sahara Desert, the Kalahari Desert in southern Africa, and the Arabian Desert on the Arabian Peninsula.

The Sahara Desert is the world's largest hot desert. It divides the continent of Africa into two parts—North Africa and sub-Saharan Africa. With temperatures soaring to nearly 122°F (50°C) during the day and falling to freezing 32°F (0°C) at night, life in the Sahara is tough. Animals and plants have to be specially adapted to survive for long periods without food or water. However, about 2.5 million people live in or around the Sahara. Rain does fall occasionally in the desert, and desert storms can be very violent. The Sahara Desert often experiences storms that produce up to 0.04 inches (1 mm) of rain per hour. The highest rainfall recorded during a Saharan storm was 1.7 inches (44 mm) in just three hours.

## DAMA GAZELLE

The dama gazelle (*Gazella dama*) is found in the Sahara Desert and the Sahel, mostly on stony plains, foothills, and arid grassland. It gets all the water it requires from eating leaves of acacia trees and desert shrubs. These gazelles move into the Sahara during the wet season and then travel south to the Sahel where they spend the dry season. This species was once the most numerous of all the gazelles in the Sahara Desert, but hunting caused its numbers to fall steeply during the 1950s to 1970s. It is also suffering the effects of desertification of the Sahel. Now it is found only in Algeria, Chad, Mali, Niger, and Sudan, and it has been reintroduced to Senegal.

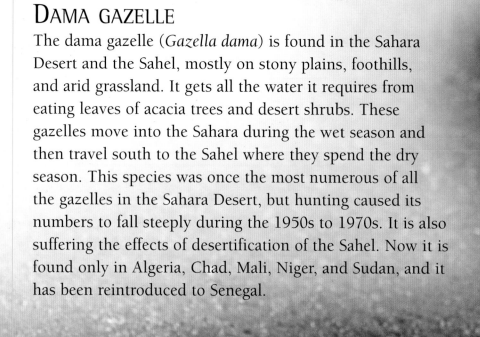

# DECLINING BIODIVERSITY

There has been a dramatic decline in biodiversity throughout the Sahara Desert, mostly due to people exploiting the few resources that exist in this harsh environment. Water is in short supply, but that has not prevented many countries from withdrawing too much for irrigating crops and supplying livestock, and that leaves little for the wildlife. There are a growing number of herds of livestock, which are overgrazing the already thin vegetation and causing widespread desertification. In addition, the large mammals are hunted with increasing ease because humans use four-wheel drive vehicles to cross the desert.

## ▲ Cheetah

The cheetah (*Acinonyx jubatus*) is the fastest land mammal in the world. It is also one of the most endangered cats in Africa. Most cheetahs are found south of the Sahara, but there are isolated populations surviving in the coastal desert and mountain ranges of the northern Sahara. Loss of habitat has reduced the number of its prey, and the cheetah has been killed because it feeds on livestock. The cheetah is protected by law throughout its range and lives within a number of nature reserves and national parks.

## ▶ Arabian oryx

The Arabian oryx (*Oryx leucoryx*) lives in herds that wander across the deserts of the Arabian Peninsula, following the rains. Its preferred habitats are flat gravel plains and areas around sandy deserts where there are trees and grasses. It can survive for weeks without drinking as it gets water from the plants it eats. This once widespread species became extinct in the wild due to overhunting, but numbers are increasing in captivity.

## ▲ Addax

One of the most endangered desert mammals is the addax (*Addax nasomaculatus*). The addax is well adapted to desert life, with wide hooves to enable it to walk on sand easily and kidneys that produce a concentrated urine, so that little water is lost from the body. Today, fewer than a couple of hundred addax remain in the wild. The addax's meat and leather are highly prized by local people, and it has been excessively hunted, using automatic weapons and all-terrain vehicles. Some of the remaining herds are protected, for example in Yotvata Hai-Bar Nature Reserve in Israel. There are also about 1,400 animals in captive-breeding programs around the world. It is hoped that one day the addax can be reintroduced to its former range.

## ◀ Gerenuk

The gerenuk (*Litocranius walleri*) gets its name from its long neck (gerenuk means "giraffe-necked" in Somali). The gerenuk can stand on its hind legs to feed on the higher leaves of trees and shrubs. It gets most of the water it needs from leaves. This species is listed as threatened due to a decrease in its population. The main threats to its survival come from habitat loss and hunting.

# Asian and Australasian Deserts

**Temperature differences**
In the Gobi Desert, in winter the average temperature is a chilly -40°F (-40°C), but in summer the average temperature is a scorching 113°F (45°C).

The Gobi is the largest desert in central Asia, extending 900 miles (1,500 km) from southwest to northeast and 500 miles (800 km) from north to south. It extends from northern China to southern Mongolia and is a cold desert, with extremely low temperatures in winter. In contrast, much of Australia is covered by hot desert, including the Great Sandy Desert and the Simpson Desert. Asia is also home to different kinds of deserts—montane deserts. These are arid places at extremely high altitudes. They are arid because they receive less than 1.5 inches (40 mm) of rainfall per year and are far from any source of moisture. Montane deserts can be found north of the Himalayas, in parts of the Kunlun Mountains, and the Tibetan Plateau.

## THE TWO-HUMPED CAMEL

The bactrian camel (*Camelus bactrianus*) is extremely well adapted for the harsh desert climate, with an ability to go for long periods without food and water. Wild bactrian camels were once found across the deserts of southern Mongolia and northwestern China, and into Kazakhstan. However, years of hunting for their meat and skin have reduced this species to just 1,000 animals in the wild. Now there are just a few populations scattered across northwest China and Mongolia. Despite being critically endangered, they are still hunted because they compete with livestock for water and grazing. The largest population is currently found in the Gobi Desert, but this population is threatened by the development of a gas pipeline and illegal mining. Nature reserves have been established to protect the remaining herds, including the Great Gobi Reserve in Mongolia and the Lop Nur Wild Camel Reserve in China. There is also a captive-breeding program run by the Wild Camel Protection Foundation.

# ALICE SPRINGS DESERT PARK

Many people think that deserts are barren places and wrongly assume that they do not need to be conserved. As a result, with much of Australia's desert wildlife under threat, it has been considered vital to educate the population about their importance. One step toward this aim was the opening of Australia's first biopark in 1997. The Alice Springs Desert Park lies in the arid center of Australia and covers an area of 3,200 acres (1,300 hectares). Its aims are to introduce people to the desert environment—to show them how aboriginal people made use of plants and animals, and to educate them on the need to conserve desert wildlife.

## ▲ Mulgara

The mulgara (*Dasycercus cristicauda*) is a carnivorous marsupial that was once widespread through the central desert region of Australia. During the heat of the day, it never emerges from its burrow. It does not need to drink, managing to obtain water from its food. This is possible because its kidneys can produce an extremely concentrated urine to conserve water. Over the years, the species has declined in population, but the causes are unclear. Fire could be a factor because it destroys vegetation. Other threats include hunting by cats and foxes and competition with cattle and rabbits. The mulgara is listed as vulnerable.

## ▶ Desert dormouse

The desert dormouse (*Selevinia betpakdalaensis*) was discovered in 1938 in the sandy deserts of Kazakhstan. It is unusual in the way it molts, losing skin and hair in patches over a period of a month. When the temperatures fall to below 41°F (5°C) the dormouse goes into hibernation to conserve energy, exactly like its relatives found in more temperate areas. It is listed as being endangered due to its restricted habitat.

## ▲ Yellow-footed rock wallaby

The yellow-footed rock wallaby (*Petrogale xanthopus*) is a marsupial and relative of the kangaroo. It is easily identified by the brown-and-yellow rings on the tail, and is found in dry rocky habitats across South Australia, western New South Wales, and southwestern Queensland. Its numbers have fallen due to competition from goats and increased hunting by the wedge-tailed eagle and introduced predators, such as cats and foxes. A conservation program is in place involving the control of goats and foxes as well as the establishment of captive-breeding programs in zoos.

## ▼ Southern marsupial mole

The solitary southern marsupial mole (*Notoryctes typhlops*) spends much of its time burrowing in sandy soil. This small animal weighs less than 2 oz (60 g), but has a powerful body that is well adapted to burrowing. It is found in the central deserts of Australia. However, this animal is very secretive so little is really known about it. Southern marsupial moles are endangered due to hunting by foxes, dingoes, and cats. Another possible threat to the survival of this species is the lack of food sources because of grazing by livestock and frequent bush fires.

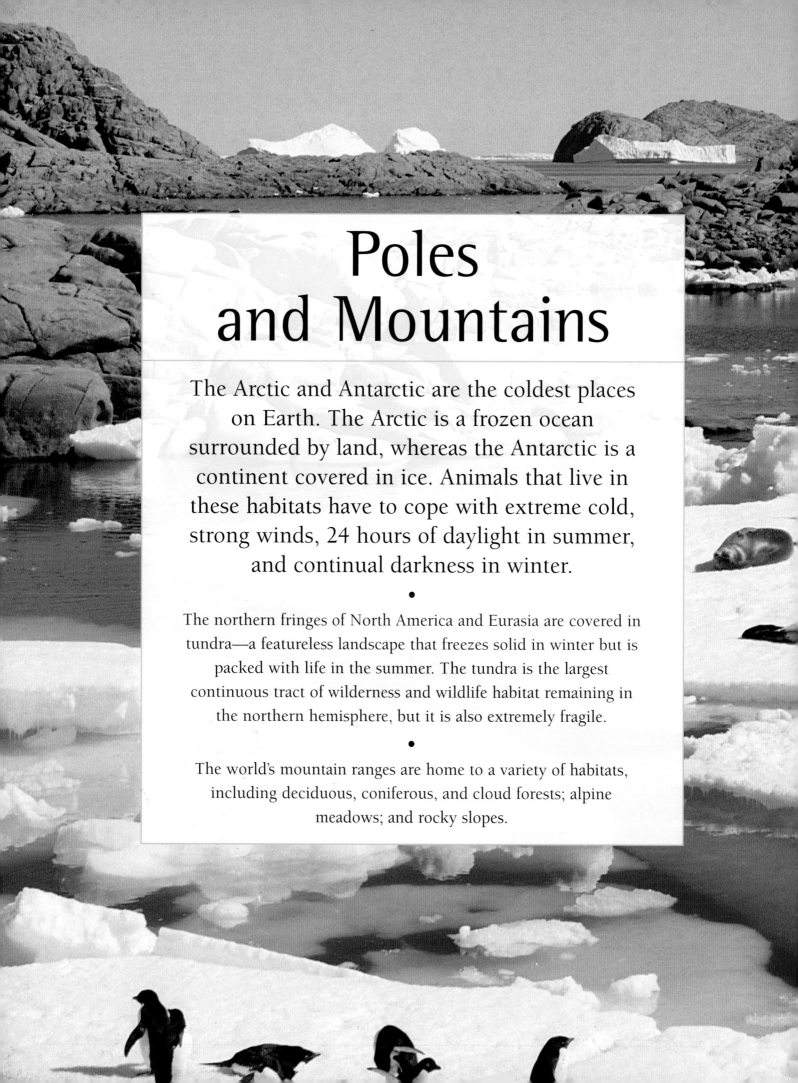

# Poles and Mountains

The Arctic and Antarctic are the coldest places on Earth. The Arctic is a frozen ocean surrounded by land, whereas the Antarctic is a continent covered in ice. Animals that live in these habitats have to cope with extreme cold, strong winds, 24 hours of daylight in summer, and continual darkness in winter.

•

The northern fringes of North America and Eurasia are covered in tundra—a featureless landscape that freezes solid in winter but is packed with life in the summer. The tundra is the largest continuous tract of wilderness and wildlife habitat remaining in the northern hemisphere, but it is also extremely fragile.

•

The world's mountain ranges are home to a variety of habitats, including deciduous, coniferous, and cloud forests; alpine meadows; and rocky slopes.

# TAIGA WILDLIFE

The taiga is the name given to the zone between the tundra and the coniferous forests that lie further south. Taiga is only found in the northern hemisphere. The trees of the taiga are shorter and not as densely packed as in the coniferous forests. In winter, many animals move south from the tundra into the taiga for shelter from the cold. During the long summer days, there are many insects and visiting birds.

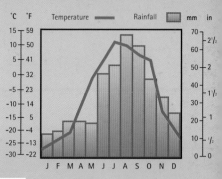

*The Siberian taiga is home to predators, such as the lynx, wolverine, bear, and mink, that prey on rabbits, squirrels, and voles. Insects attract insect-eating birds that breed in the taiga in summer and then fly south in winter. Seed-eating birds such as finches and sparrows remain all year.*

## Rainfall

In taiga regions, the rainfall is low, with most falling during the summer months. In winter, there are a few snowfalls.

## Temperature

During the Arctic winter the average temperatures fall to about -22°F (-30°C). The temperatures creep above freezing after May, reaching an average of about 54°F (12°C) in July, before falling back below freezing in October.

# HABITATS AT RISK

Both mountain and polar habitats are at risk from human activities. There has been extensive deforestation in both the mountains and taiga. Remote Arctic areas are being explored for oil and gas. However, an even bigger threat faces the polar regions: global warming. As the earth gets warmer as a result of more greenhouse gases trapping heat in the atmosphere, the polar ice caps are beginning to melt, putting animals such as penguins and polar bears at risk.

*This Himalayan mountain slope has been cleared of forest, leaving the soil at risk of being washed away in heavy rain.*

# Tundra, Poles, and Mountains

The polar regions are found at the very top and bottom of the globe. To the south of the Arctic is a barren region called the tundra and then a belt of forest called the taiga. The world's great mountain chains include the Himalayas in Asia and the Andes and Rockies in the Americas.

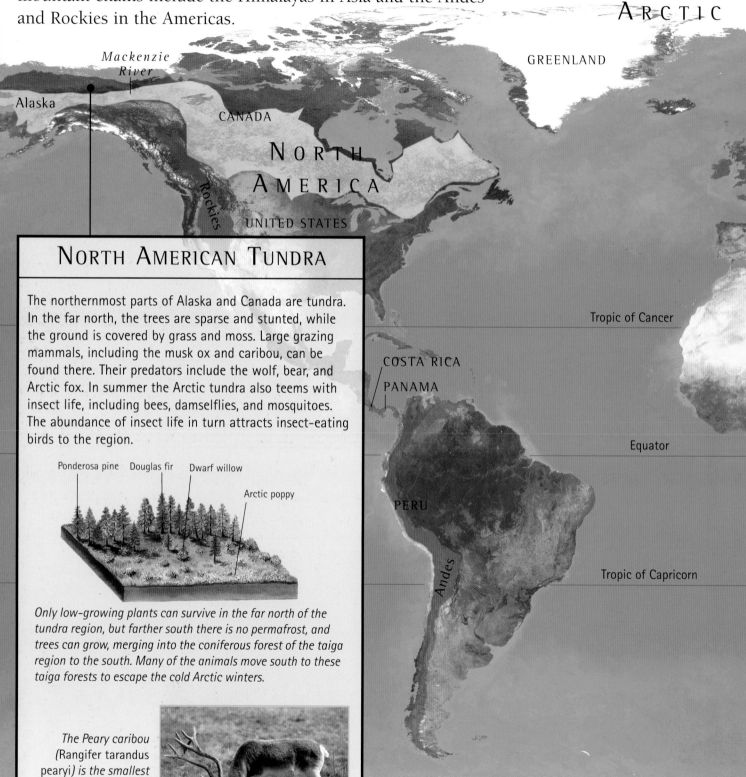

ARCTIC

GREENLAND

Mackenzie River

Alaska

CANADA

NORTH AMERICA

Rockies

UNITED STATES

Tropic of Cancer

COSTA RICA

PANAMA

PERU

Andes

Equator

Tropic of Capricorn

ANTARCTICA

## NORTH AMERICAN TUNDRA

The northernmost parts of Alaska and Canada are tundra. In the far north, the trees are sparse and stunted, while the ground is covered by grass and moss. Large grazing mammals, including the musk ox and caribou, can be found there. Their predators include the wolf, bear, and Arctic fox. In summer the Arctic tundra also teems with insect life, including bees, damselflies, and mosquitoes. The abundance of insect life in turn attracts insect-eating birds to the region.

Ponderosa pine    Douglas fir    Dwarf willow

Arctic poppy

*Only low-growing plants can survive in the far north of the tundra region, but farther south there is no permafrost, and trees can grow, merging into the coniferous forest of the taiga region to the south. Many of the animals move south to these taiga forests to escape the cold Arctic winters.*

*The Peary caribou (Rangifer tarandus pearyi) is the smallest of all caribou and is found only in Canada, where less than 2,000 of the animals survive.*

## EURASIAN TAIGA

Tundra and taiga cover northern Norway, Finland, and Russia. Here there are herds of reindeer and musk ox, as well as small herbivores such as hares, lemmings, ground squirrels, and marmots. Among their natural predators are brown bears and wolverines.

Spruce, fir, pine          Juniper

*The belt of taiga consists of coniferous forests. Trees include spruce, fir, and pine. To the north is the tundra, where little covers the ground but mosses.*

*Wolverines (Gulo gulo) are members of the weasel family. They are renowned for their strength, ferocity, and fearlessness.*

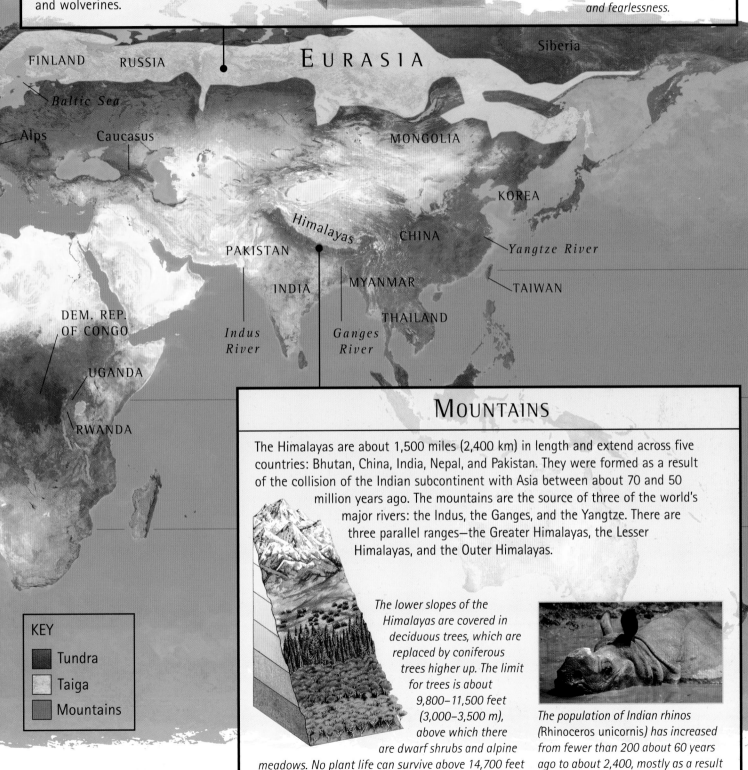

FINLAND     RUSSIA

*Baltic Sea*

Alps     Caucasus

E U R A S I A

Siberia

MONGOLIA

KOREA

PAKISTAN

*Himalayas*     CHINA

*Yangtze River*

INDIA     MYANMAR

TAIWAN

THAILAND

DEM. REP. OF CONGO

*Indus River*     *Ganges River*

UGANDA

RWANDA

**KEY**
- Tundra
- Taiga
- Mountains

## MOUNTAINS

The Himalayas are about 1,500 miles (2,400 km) in length and extend across five countries: Bhutan, China, India, Nepal, and Pakistan. They were formed as a result of the collision of the Indian subcontinent with Asia between about 70 and 50 million years ago. The mountains are the source of three of the world's major rivers: the Indus, the Ganges, and the Yangtze. There are three parallel ranges—the Greater Himalayas, the Lesser Himalayas, and the Outer Himalayas.

*The lower slopes of the Himalayas are covered in deciduous trees, which are replaced by coniferous trees higher up. The limit for trees is about 9,800–11,500 feet (3,000–3,500 m), above which there are dwarf shrubs and alpine meadows. No plant life can survive above 14,700 feet (4,500 m), so the peaks are bare.*

*The population of Indian rhinos (Rhinoceros unicornis) has increased from fewer than 200 about 60 years ago to about 2,400, mostly as a result of increased protection from poachers.*

69

# Poles, Tundra, and Taiga

Life at the ends of the world is very tough. Polar animals have adapted to the extreme cold, the perpetual darkness in winter, and the continual light in summer. Many of these animals are not found anywhere else in the world. However, many are at risk of extinction due to global warming, which is melting the ice and destroying habitats. Those at risk include the world's largest land predator—the polar bear.

## The Poles

The North Pole is the northernmost point of the planet. It lies in the ice-packed Arctic Ocean. Earth's southernmost point, the South Pole, is located on the continent of Antarctica.

## STELLAR'S EIDER

Stellar's eider (*Polysticta stelleri*) is a large sea duck whose feathers provide excellent insulation from the cold. During the breeding season, this bird is found on open tundra, close to pools and lakes. There it builds a nest that it lines with feathers. In winter it flies south to warmer rocky coasts along the Bering Sea, northern Scandinavia, and the Baltic Sea. Stellar's eider has suffered from the effects of increasing pollutants in the water, which have reduced its breeding success. It is also hunted for its high-quality feathers, for use in products such as pillows. As a result, Stellar's eider is protected in most Arctic countries, including the United States and Russia. The United States Fish and Wildlife Service has designated a large area of Alaskan coastline as a protected area for the bird's conservation.

# POLAR THREATS

Although the Arctic is remote and bitterly cold for much of the year, it is still threatened by the activities of people. The Arctic holds the world's largest remaining undeveloped gas and oil reserves, so not surprisingly many companies are looking to exploit the region. Four areas are already under threat—the Arctic National Wildlife Refuge in Alaska, the Barents Sea, the Canadian Low Arctic Tundra, and the Mackenzie River Valley and Delta in Canada. Oil and gas extraction involves mining for gravel and constructing new roads and pipelines. All these activities cause habitat destruction for wildlife.

## ▲ Polar bear

The magnificent polar bear (*Ursus maritimus*) is one of the best-known animals in the world. It is the largest living land predator. This bear is well adapted to life in the Arctic, with thick fur and a layer of fat to keep it warm. Polar bears are found throughout the Arctic, including Canada, Norway, parts of Alaska in the United States, and Russia. The world population is between 20,000 and 25,000, with about 60 percent living in Canada. The main threats to this species are climate change—which is causing the sea ice to break up earlier in the season than normal; fishing and hunting; and pollution, drilling, and mining in the Arctic. Canada, Norway, the United States, Russia, and Denmark have all signed an agreement to conserve the bears. They have banned hunting (with specific exceptions for some indigenous peoples) and given protection to the migration routes and nursery areas.

## ▼ Wolverine

The wolverine (*Gulo gulo*) is the largest member of the weasel family and is found from the western United States (mainly Alaska) and Canada to Siberia, eastern Europe, and Scandinavia. The wolverine has declined through much of its range as it is easily disturbed by people. It continues to suffer from habitat loss and from competition from other predators, such as the wolf. It is also killed by farmers because it attacks livestock. It is listed as being vulnerable.

## ► European elk

The European elk or moose (*Alces alces*) is the largest member of the deer family. It has long legs, large flattened antlers, and a long snout. It occurs from Norway and Sweden to Russia and Siberia and across Canada and the northernmost states of the United States, including Alaska and Maine. There is also a small population of elk in Poland. In some areas, elk populations have been greatly reduced by human hunting and habitat destruction. However, elk have been reintroduced in some areas. For example, the elk was reintroduced to the Kampinos Forest in Poland in 1958, and these animals have bred successfully and spread out across Poland.

## ▲ Arctic fox

The fur of the Arctic fox (*Alopex lagopus*) provides the best insulation of any mammal, and even the soles of its feet are covered with a layer of hair to prevent frostbite. This fox changes color during the year—in winter its coat is white, but in summer it changes to a gray-brown. There are several hundred thousand foxes in the Arctic, and their numbers go up and down according to the number of their favorite prey, lemmings. In most of its range, the Arctic fox is not protected, and it is hunted for its fur, especially the white fur, which is particularly valuable. Arctic foxes are also under threat from diseases carried by domestic dogs.

# The Himalayas

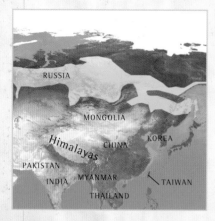

**Dramatic landscape**
The Himalayas are the source of several great rivers, and they also have the largest concentration of glaciers outside of the North and South Poles.

The Himalayas are the world's highest mountain range. Fourteen of the world's highest peaks are found there, including the world's tallest mountain—Mount Everest. Mount Everest stands 29,035 feet (8,850 m) tall. The world's second tallest mountain, K2, is also located in the Himalayas. K2 is 28,251 feet (8,611 m) tall. There are a variety of habitats in the Himalayas, including deciduous and coniferous forests, alpine meadows, and rocky slopes. The Himalaya-Tibet region helps to supply nearly one-fifth of the world's population with fresh water. However, some of the world's most endangered animals are also found among the Himalayan peaks.

## KILLED FOR PERFUME

The Siberian musk deer (*Moschus moschiferus*) is found in the mountainous forests of Asia, including Russia, Korea, China, and through the Himalayas to northern India and Pakistan. It is a small deer and does not have antlers. The male deer produces musk (a strong-smelling, brown, waxy substance), which is used in the manufacture of perfume, soap, and some Chinese medicines. Musk is highly valued, with 2 pounds (1 kg) fetching as much as $45,000, so the males have been heavily hunted. It is possible to extract the musk from live animals, but most of the hunters kill the animal to remove all the musk. A single animal yields about 1 ounce (25 g) of musk, which is worth more than $1,000. It is hoped that hunters can be taught how to trap the deer and obtain the musk without harming the animal. In that way, hunters would have a sustainable harvest. The species is listed as vulnerable, but the size of the population is unknown.

# FUTURE OF THE FORESTS

Over the last 60 years, there has been wide-scale deforestation in the Himalayas. Trees are cut down for firewood by local people and for timber by large companies. When the trees are cleared, rain water washes down the bare slopes and carries away the soil. This causes flooding in the river valleys and also affects the water supply downstream. Normally the forests hold water in the ground, letting it drain away gradually, and this ensures a year-round supply of water. Without the trees the water runs straight into the rivers, and later in the year the rivers may run dry. To prevent this, many replanting schemes are under way, and people have set up tree nurseries to supply saplings for the new forests.

## ▲ Snow leopard

The snow leopard (*Uncia uncia*) has smoky-gray fur patterned with gray-black spots. This predator lives high in the mountains, on ridges and rocky outcrops, as well as on the grasslands of central Asia. It preys on wild sheep, goats, birds, and hares. Its decline is due to hunting for its fur; a pelt is worth up to 60 times the average annual wage in China. The leopard is also hunted because it preys on livestock and its bones are used in some traditional Chinese medicines. There are between 4,500 and 7,400 snow leopards left in the wild, and the species is listed as endangered despite several conservation programs.

## ▶ Red panda

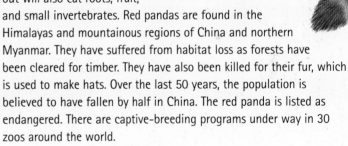

The red panda (*Ailurus fulgens*) is a type of raccoon found in dense mountain forests at altitudes between 6,000 and 13,000 feet (1,800 and 4,000 m). It feeds mostly on bamboo shoots but will also eat roots, fruit, and small invertebrates. Red pandas are found in the Himalayas and mountainous regions of China and northern Myanmar. They have suffered from habitat loss as forests have been cleared for timber. They have also been killed for their fur, which is used to make hats. Over the last 50 years, the population is believed to have fallen by half in China. The red panda is listed as endangered. There are captive-breeding programs under way in 30 zoos around the world.

## ◀ Himalayan tahr

The Himalayan tahr (*Hemitragus jemlahicus*) is related to the wild goat. It has flexible hooves with hard rims which can grip smooth rocks and small footholds. It is found in the southern Himalayas, from northern India to Bhutan. The tahr has suffered from habitat loss, increased competition from sheep and goats, and overhunting for both sport and meat. It lives in a number of protected areas, including the Great Himalayan National Park, and there are plans to establish the Srikhand National Park as a reserve for tahr. This species is listed as vulnerable.

## ▼ Wild yak

Wild yaks (*Bos grunniens*) are large animals with humped shoulders. Both males and females have horns that they use to dig through the snow to find food. Wild yaks are found in remote mountains from Kashmir to China, up to 19,700 feet (6,000 m). Their numbers have fallen due to habitat loss and hunting. The wild yak is protected in China and India, but this is difficult to enforce because of the remote locations.

## ◀ Serow

The serow (*Capricornis sumatraensis*) is a goatlike animal with a short body, long legs, and small horns. An unusual feature is the large tear pockets that can be clearly seen under the eyes. Serows are found in the Himalayas from Kashmir to south China and Myanmar. Some remain in Thailand, Malaysia, and Sumatra. The serow's numbers are declining due to habitat loss caused by deforestation and the expansion of agriculture. The serow has also been hunted for its meat. It is listed as being vulnerable.

# Cloud Forest

Cloud forests are unique ecosystems that occur only in specific tropical mountain areas. The unusual weather conditions have created a habitat for thousands of plants and animals that can be found nowhere else on Earth. However, these forests are among the world's most threatened environments.

### Head in the clouds
Cloud forests get their name from the low-level clouds that are found around the canopy of the rain forest. They are also called Afromontane forests and upper montane rain forests.

## THE MOUNTAIN GORILLA

The mountain gorilla (*Gorilla beringei beringei*) is only found on the forested slopes of the Virunga Range of volcanoes on the borders of Rwanda, Uganda, and the Democratic Republic of Congo. This gorilla has long, shaggy fur to keep it warm during the cold nights. There are fewer than 400 mountain gorillas, living in small family groups led by a dominant male. Most gorillas live within national parks and are protected by armed guards. In the past many gorillas were killed and their young sold as pets. A new threat has come from the tourists who visit the national parks to see the gorillas—as they come into close contact with them, there is a chance that the gorillas could catch human diseases. The mountain gorilla is listed as critically endangered.

# Monteverde: a special place

The Monteverde cloud forest is found high in the mountains of Costa Rica in Central America. Here it is always misty, and humidity is high. The trees are covered with plants called epiphytes, including mosses, ferns, bromeliads, and orchids. These forests are home to almost 900 different types of epiphytes, including 450 species of orchids. Much of the cloud forest is protected, and one of the first nature reserves, the Monteverde Cloud Forest Reserve, extends over 25,000 acres (10,000 hectares). A replanting program is under way on the lower slopes.

## ▲ Sumatran short-eared rabbit

The Sumatran short-eared rabbit (*Nesolagus netscheri*) is a nocturnal animal that is found only in remote mountain forests of the Barisan Mountains of Sumatra, Indonesia. During the day it shelters in holes, and at night it emerges to feed on leaves. This rabbit is thought to be critically endangered, but very little is known about it. Very few have ever been spotted, and the last sighting was in 1998. The rabbit is so rare that local people are unaware that it exists. The main threats come from the clearing of forest for tea and coffee plantations.

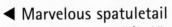

## ◀ Marvelous spatuletail

The marvelous spatuletail (*Loddigesia mirabilis*) is a type of hummingbird named after its amazing tail. It is found in a single remote valley in northern Peru, where it flies along forest edges, feeding on nectar from yellow-flowered trees. It is listed as endangered because of the deforestation that has taken place on the hillsides where it lives. Now there are fewer trees with the yellow flowers on which it feeds, and its numbers have decreased. The conservation of this species should start with the protection of its habitat.

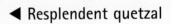

## ◀ Resplendent quetzal

Many people consider the resplendent quetzal (*Pharomachrus mocinno*) to be one of the most beautiful birds in the world. The males have spectacular tail feathers that are more than 20 inches (50 cm) in length. Quetzals are found from southern Mexico to Panama, with one of the largest populations being found in the Monteverde cloud forest of Costa Rica. The birds do not stay in one place all year round but migrate to other areas of forest. This makes their conservation difficult as more habitats have to be protected to ensure their survival. The quetzal is the only bird that is able to eat the fruit of the wild avocado. The wild avocado relies on the quetzals to disperse its seeds, so any threat to the bird species also affects the future of the fruit.

## ▼ Spectacled bear

The spectacled bear (*Tremarctos ornatus*) gets its name from the white rings round its eyes. There is also a unique pattern of creamy-yellow markings down its chest. This small bear is found throughout the Andes in South America, living in cloud forest, high-altitude grassland, and scrub. It is estimated that fewer than 2,000 survive, and it is listed as vulnerable. The main cause of its decline is loss of habitat. The bears are also hunted for their meat, skin, and claws. Trade in this species and its body parts is banned, but poachers can still earn more than $100 for a gall bladder, which is used in some traditional Chinese medicines.

# Oceans and Islands

Oceans cover more than two-thirds of the earth's surface and reach depths of 3½ miles (6 km). Compared with land, this watery habitat is hardly explored, yet it is more complex than any land-based habitat. Many of the world's islands are home to unique collections of plants and animals.

•

The shallow waters around the continents (continental shelf) are among the most productive waters in the world because they are rich in nutrients and receive plenty of light. Coral reefs, found around some tropical coasts, have the greatest range of species of all the marine habitats. The open ocean is much deeper, and light does not penetrate more than 820 ft (250 m) below the surface. Most of the animals are found in the surface layer—below this, the water is cold and dark, and only a few animals can survive. The seabed is criss-crossed with folds and troughs, and it is rich in life. Many species live in, on, or just above the sediment and feed on dead and decaying matter that sinks down from above.

# ISLAND WILDLIFE

Many islands have their own unique collections of plants and animals that are not found anywhere else. This is because islands are often isolated, lying hundreds of miles from the nearest mainland. Plants and animals are carried to these islands by wind and water. Gradually they adapt to the conditions that exist on the islands and develop in a different way from other individuals of the same species that can be found on the mainland.

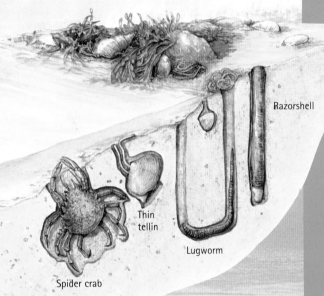

*Coastal areas are regularly submerged and exposed by the advancing and retreating tides. Many creatures have learned to adapt to this changing environment by burying themselves in the sand.*

Common mussel

Common cockle

Sand gaper

Spider crab

Thin tellin

Lugworm

Razorshell

## Rainfall

The months with the highest rainfall in the Galápagos Islands, in the Pacific Ocean, coincide with the highest temperatures. The driest months are in autumn (September to December).

## Temperature

The Galápagos Islands have a tropical climate, so the temperatures range between 72 and 82°F (22 and 28°C), with the hottest months in winter.

*Oil spills can kill thousands of sea birds as well as marine mammals and invertebrate life, such as crabs.*

# THREATS TO THE OCEANS

The main threats to marine habitats are pollution and overfishing. For a long time, people have dumped their waste in the water, including garbage, sewage, industrial effluents, and even radioactive wastes. There are oil spills, too. Pollution dumped into rivers ends up in the oceans. People have fished the seas for thousands of years, but the rise in the human population and improved methods of fishing are seriously threatening fish stocks in all the oceans.

# Oceans and Islands

There are five oceans—the Atlantic, Arctic, Indian, Pacific, and Southern Ocean.
The Southern Ocean was established in 2000 by designating the southernmost areas of
the Atlantic and Pacific Oceans as
the Southern Ocean.

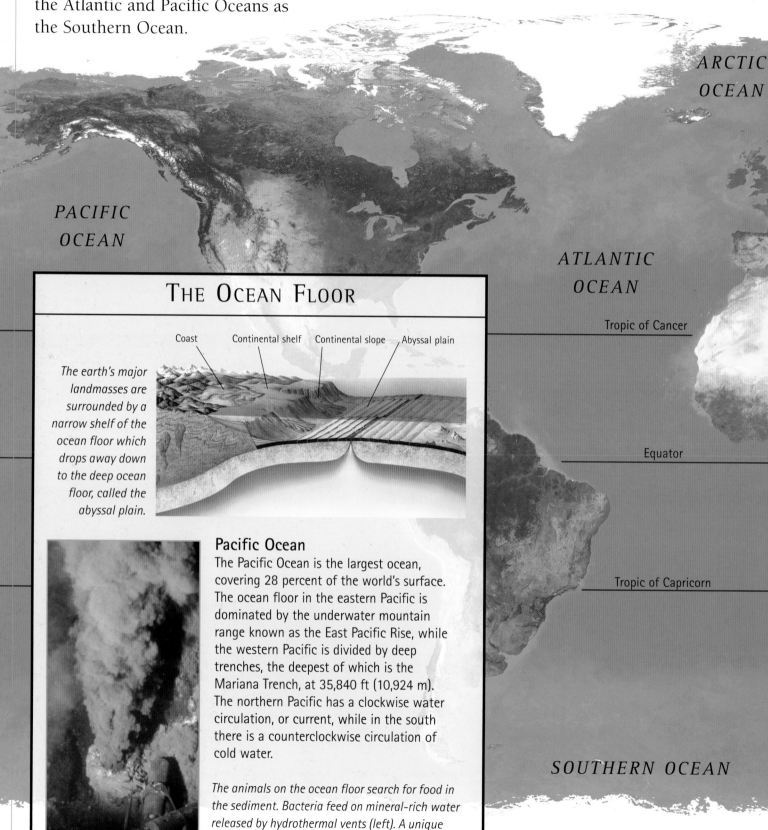

ARCTIC OCEAN

PACIFIC OCEAN

ATLANTIC OCEAN

Tropic of Cancer

Equator

Tropic of Capricorn

SOUTHERN OCEAN

## THE OCEAN FLOOR

The earth's major landmasses are surrounded by a narrow shelf of the ocean floor which drops away down to the deep ocean floor, called the abyssal plain.

Coast    Continental shelf    Continental slope    Abyssal plain

### Pacific Ocean

The Pacific Ocean is the largest ocean, covering 28 percent of the world's surface. The ocean floor in the eastern Pacific is dominated by the underwater mountain range known as the East Pacific Rise, while the western Pacific is divided by deep trenches, the deepest of which is the Mariana Trench, at 35,840 ft (10,924 m). The northern Pacific has a clockwise water circulation, or current, while in the south there is a counterclockwise circulation of cold water.

The animals on the ocean floor search for food in the sediment. Bacteria feed on mineral-rich water released by hydrothermal vents (left). A unique group of animals, such as giant tube worms, clams, and crabs, are found around these vents.

# ISLANDS

## Forming islands

Some islands are formed as a result of volcanic activity. For example, the Hawaiian Islands are a chain of eight islands in the middle of the Pacific Ocean. The islands are the tops of giant undersea volcanoes, some of which are still active. Some islands are created when they are cut off from the mainland by rising sea levels, while others are created by coral animals.

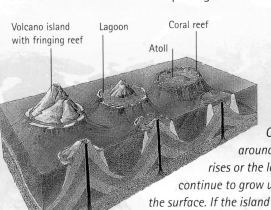

Volcano island with fringing reef — Lagoon — Coral reef — Atoll

*Corals can form a reef around an island. If the sea level rises or the land mass sinks, the corals continue to grow upward, staying just under the surface. If the island disappears below sea level, a ring of coral remains with a lagoon in the middle. This is called an atoll. Atolls may take 30 million years to form.*

*The Hawaiian goose or ne ne (Nesochen sandvicensis) is part of a captive-breeding program.*

*PACIFIC OCEAN*

*INDIAN OCEAN*

Mariana Trench

# THE GREAT BARRIER REEF

## Coral reef

The world's largest coral reef system is the Great Barrier Reef, off the northeastern coast of Australia. It is about 1,249 miles (2,010 km) long. There are about 3,000 individual reefs and 300 coral islands. It represents 13 percent of the world's coral reef. In 1975, the Great Barrier Reef Marine Park was established, and in 1981, it was designated a World Heritage Site.

Great Barrier Reef

AUSTRALIA

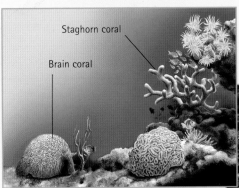

Staghorn coral

Brain coral

*Barrier reefs act as natural breakwaters and protect the coasts from storm surges.*

*Green turtles (Chelonia mydas) are regularly seen on coral reefs. They are a protected species.*

NEW ZEALAND

# The Atlantic Ocean

The Atlantic Ocean is the second largest of the world's oceans, after the Pacific. It extends from the Southern Ocean to the Arctic. The Mid-Atlantic Ridge is an underwater mountain chain that dominates the ocean floor. The major current in the Atlantic is the Gulf Stream, a warm-water current originating in the Gulf of Mexico and flowing north along the eastern coast of North America before crossing the Atlantic Ocean to Western Europe and North Africa.

**Atlantic currents**

In the South Atlantic, a warm-water current flows south along the coast of South America, and a cold current flows north along the African coast. In the North Atlantic, the warm Gulf Stream flows eastward.

## THE NORTHERN RIGHT WHALE

The northern right whale (*Eubalaena glacialis*) is a massive whale, mostly black, with patches of white on its underside. The head is encrusted with barnacles and whale lice. The northern right whale is the most endangered of the baleen whales. It gets its name from whalers who considered it to be the "right" whale to hunt. This is because the whales swim slowly and are easy to catch; the dead whales float, and their bodies contain large quantities of oil and baleen (whalebone). So many whales were caught that the species almost became extinct in the 1800s. Although hunting has been banned since 1935, only a couple hundred whales remain. These whales are still at risk from collisions with ships and fishing gear because they like to feed near the surface in busy coastal waters. Conservation measures include the closing of certain fishing areas and the modification of fishing gear. Key areas off the eastern coast of North America have been designated as critical right whale habitat and are likely to be given extra protection.

# IMPORTANCE OF FISH

The Atlantic Ocean is one of the most heavily fished oceans. Waters around northern Europe and off the eastern coast of North America have been commercially fished for hundreds of years, and stocks of fish such as cod, haddock, and herring have almost collapsed. The European Union, Iceland, Canada, and United States all have fishing controls and quotas in place, but these fish are found all across the Atlantic, and it is difficult to control fishing in international waters. Fish are critical to the health of ocean food chains; when their numbers fall, species that are dependent upon them fall, too.

### ▶ Rainbow parrotfish

The rainbow parrotfish (*Scarus guacamaia*) is the largest herbivorous fish in the Atlantic, with males growing to lengths of 4 ft (1.2 m). This brightly colored fish has a hard parrot-like beak with which to scrape algae from the surface of coral. Young parrotfish are found in mangrove swamps, but the adults live on coral reefs. This species is listed as vulnerable, largely due to the loss of mangrove swamp and coral reef.

### ◀ Dwarf seahorse

Dwarf seahorses (*Hippocampus zosterae*) live in sea grass along the coasts of Texas, Florida, and the Bahamas. Seahorses are unusual fish—not only is their body shape different from other fish, but the female places her eggs in a special pouch on the male's abdomen, and he looks after them until they hatch. Their habitat is under threat from water pollution, dredging, and coastal development. They also become caught in shrimp nets.

### ▲ Basking shark

The basking shark (*Cetorhinus maximus*) is the second largest fish after the whale shark. It swims with its wide mouth open so that it can take in large volumes of water. As the water passes through its gills, plankton and other animals are sieved out. Basking sharks travel alone or in groups of up to 100. They prefer to swim in temperate coastal waters where there is plenty of plankton. This shark is vulnerable to overfishing because it grows slowly and takes a long time to reproduce.

### ◀ Atlantic cod

The Atlantic cod (*Gadus morhua*) lives in huge shoals on the continental shelf, feeding on smaller fish such as herring and sprats. It is heavily overfished, and in 2001, numbers fell to an historic low. During that year, much of the North Sea was closed to fishing fleets as part of an emergency protection plan. Conservation programs include no-catch zones, protected spawning areas, and the modification of fishing nets so that young fish cannot be caught. Currently, only cod caught in Icelandic waters are regarded as being sustainably fished.

### ▲ Atlantic salmon

Atlantic salmon (*Salmo salar*) start life as tiny fish in the freshwater rivers of North America and Europe. They migrate to the North Atlantic, where they spend up to four years feeding and growing. When they are ready to breed, they return to the river of their birth. The Atlantic salmon is a highly prized food fish, and the species has suffered from overfishing, especially at sea. In 1966, Canada, the United States, and Spain banned fishing of salmon at sea. Other countries joined the ban a few years later. There are other threats too, including acid rain damage to the rivers where they breed.

### ▼ Hogfish

The hogfish (*Lachnolaimus maximus*) is found from Nova Scotia to northern South America, although it is most numerous in warm waters. This large fish feeds by day on invertebrates such as crabs, bivalves, and gastropods. Due to overfishing, the hogfish has been listed as vulnerable.

# The Pacific Ocean

**Vast ocean**

The Pacific Ocean is approximately 10,936 miles (17,600 km) wide at the equator. It has an average depth of 2.5 miles (4 km).

The Pacific is the world's largest ocean. It is surrounded by a zone of volcanic and earthquake activity, often referred to as the "Ring of Fire." Volcanic eruptions are frequent, while tsunamis, caused by underwater earthquakes, have devastated many islands and wiped out whole towns. The Pacific also experiences typhoons in the tropical regions. This ocean contains about 25,000 islands, which is more than the total number of islands in the rest of the world's oceans combined. The majority of these islands are found south of the equator.

## GIANT CLAM

The giant clam (*Tridacna spp.*) is the largest and heaviest of the clams, growing to more than 4 ft (1.2 m) in length. It is a bivalve, with two thick shells that cannot close completely. It is found on shallow reefs to depths of 66 ft (20 m) throughout the southern Pacific and Indian Oceans. Once a giant clam settles into place and begins to grow, it stays permanently attached to that spot for life, filtering food from the water. Giant clams have been harvested for their meat and to supply the aquarium trade. However, this harvest has been unsustainable, and populations are showing signs of decline. The giant clam is now specially farmed, and it is hoped that this will reduce the pressure on the wild populations. Some farmed clams have been introduced to reefs around Tonga, where numbers were very low.

# THREATS TO WILDLIFE

The Pacific Ocean is home to a wide range of species, especially on coral reefs such as the Great Barrier Reef. However, pollution and climate change threaten to disrupt this enormous environment. Coral reefs are only found in warm water where there is plenty of light, and the coral animals are very susceptible to change. A slight rise in temperature can cause the algae that live within the corals to leave. The corals then become white, a process called bleaching. This has happened on reefs across the Pacific Ocean. In addition, mangrove swamps along many tropical coasts have been cleared. These habitats are important fish nurseries, and their clearance has reduced fish stocks.

## ▲ Humpback whale

The humpback whale (*Megaptera novaeangliae*) is well known for its impressive displays of leaping out of the water and for the songs of the males. Whaling in the Southern Hemisphere during the first half of the 20th century resulted in more than 100,000 humpbacks being slaughtered. They were given protection in 1966, and their numbers have since increased. However, these magnificent whales are vulnerable to changes in the marine environment, especially those caused by pollution and global warming. They are also affected by the availability of their food—krill and fish.

## ▶ Steller's sea lion

The largest of the eared seals is the Steller's sea lion (*Eumetopias jubatus*). The males are much larger than the females, with thick necks, and shoulders covered in long, coarse hair. The world population of this marine mammal has fallen from 300,000 to 100,000 since 1980, but the causes are unclear. Marine pollution, disease, and disturbance to the breeding colonies have all been blamed. However, some scientists believe that it is due to a change in their diet. They are eating more low-energy fish, which causes them to lose weight, which in turn reduces their fertility and their ability to survive disease.

## ▲ Great white shark

The great white shark (*Carcharodon carcharias*) is one of the most powerful hunters of the oceans. It has a reputation as a man-eater, and has a large mouth full of sharply pointed, jagged teeth. The population has fallen by as much as 20 percent over the last few years. Great whites are caught on baited fishing lines or fished for their meat, skin, oil, teeth, jaws, and their fins for shark-fin soup. This shark is protected in South Africa, Namibia, the Maldives, Australia, and the states of California and Florida. Diving with great whites is popular, so the tourist trade may become an important way of conserving this species.

## ◀ Wandering albatross

The wandering albatross (*Diomedea exulans*) has a wingspan of up to 11.5 ft (3.5 m), the largest of any bird. It is found in the southern Pacific Ocean, where it glides over the surface of the water looking for squid. The main threat to this species is long-line fishing, as the birds get caught on the baited hooks and drown. Breeding pairs only raise one chick every other year, so their numbers are slow to recover.

## ▼ Bluntnose six–gilled shark

Most sharks have five gill slits on either side of their head. The bluntnose six-gill shark (*Hexanchus griseus*) has a blunt, rounded snout with six gill slits. This shark is a deep-water species that feeds on rays, squid, and fish. It is widespread and relatively abundant. However, its numbers are falling due to overfishing, and now it is likely that it will be listed as vulnerable. This shark is slow to reproduce, so any overfishing means that it will take time for numbers to recover.

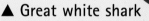

## ▶ Hawksbill turtle

The yellow, orange, and brown shell of the hawksbill turtle (*Eretmochelys imbricata*) is the reason that is has been hunted for thousands of years. Numbers have fallen by as much as 80 percent over the last hundred years. It is critically endangered.

# Polar Waters

ARCTIC OCEAN
GREENLAND
ICELAND
ATLANTIC OCEAN

**Chilly northern waters**
The Arctic Ocean is the smallest of the world's oceans, covering an area of 5,440,000 square miles (14,090,000 square km).

The Arctic Ocean is almost completely enclosed by land. The central part, around the North Pole, is permanently covered by about 10 ft (3 m) of ice. The Southern Ocean extends from the Antarctic to where the cold Antarctic water meets warm water flowing south from the tropics. The waters of both oceans are icy cold, but they are filled with life at certain times of year. During the spring and summer, the water is full of plankton, which attracts animals such as whales.

## THE GIANT OF THE OCEANS

The blue whale (*Balaenoptera musculus*) is the largest animal ever to have lived. It lives in the Atlantic, Pacific, Arctic, and Indian Oceans, with a range that extends from the edge of the ice pack to the tropics. These whales swim quickly for their size, and as a result, were not caught by whalers until the 1920s. Over the next 40 years, so many were slaughtered that they were on the brink of extinction until hunting was banned in 1966. However, the population does not seem to be recovering, and fewer than 5,000 remain. It is likely that marine pollution, shrinking fish stocks, and illegal whaling are to blame.

# PROTECTING THE ANTARCTIC

Until the 19th century, Antarctica had never been visited by people. It was a huge, unspoiled wilderness. The challenge now is to keep it in as good a state as possible. After World War II, a number of countries established research stations and laid claim to territory. In 1959, the Antarctic Treaty was drawn up to protect the continent and allow scientific work to continue. In 1998, the Protocol on Environmental Protection to the Antarctic treaty came into force. It protects the Antarctic environment and prohibits any activities relating to mineral resources. However, there are other threats to this unique habitat, in particular global warming, which is causing part of the ice sheet to break up.

## ▼ Walrus

The walrus (*Odobenus rosmarus*) lives in open water at the edge of the Arctic ice. Its characteristic feature is its pair of long tusks. The walrus's skin is thick, wrinkled, and nearly hairless. Males grow to just under 13 ft (4 m) in length and may weigh as much as 3,086 lbs (1,400 kg). Commercial hunting of walruses for blubber, hides, and ivory (tusks) has taken place since the 16th century. This has greatly reduced the walrus population. Canada and Russia prohibit walrus hunting except by people for whom it is a traditional way of life.

## ▶ Northern fur seal

Northern fur seals (*Callorhinus ursinus*) have a thick fur that protects them from the Arctic cold. Unfortunately, this fur was much desired by people, and as a result, they were hunted for centuries. Commercial hunting during the 19th century nearly caused the seals to become extinct. In 1911, a treaty was drawn up to protect them. This enabled the population to recover, and it now stands at about 1,350,000 animals. Today the main threats to the seals are entanglement in nets of Japanese fishing fleets as well as in discarded nets. They are very vulnerable to marine pollution, especially from oil spills.

## ▲ Bowhead whale

The bowhead whale (*Balaena mysticetus*) is named after its bow-shaped mouth. It has a mostly black body and a white chin patch with a row of black spots. It stays near the ice of the Arctic all year using its echolocation to navigate through the ice. This whale was heavily hunted until hunting was banned in 1966. The main threats to this species are marine pollution, entanglement in fishing nets, and collisions with ships. The numbers of the bowhead whale are increasing in some areas, and small-scale hunting by the Inuits of Canada is still allowed.

## ▲ Beluga (white whale)

The white skin of the beluga (*Delphinapterus leucas*) makes it very easy to identify. The calves are born dark gray, and they develop their white color as they age. The beluga is a toothed whale that stays close to the edge of the Arctic ice. Belugas have been hunted for their blubber for hundreds of years, but it was only during the 20th century that their numbers fell. The greatest risk to this species today is marine pollution. Belugas living in the St. Lawrence River estuary accumulate so many toxins that deformed calves are common, and dead belugas are treated as toxic waste. Hunting is banned, but the Inuits are allowed small quotas.

## ▼ Killer whale (orca)

The orca, or killer whale (*Orcinus orca*) is the largest toothed whale. It has black and white markings, and a distinctive grayish-white area called a saddle-patch behind its dorsal fin. This predator of seals, turtles, birds, and fish (including sharks) is threatened by pollution, hunting, loss of food supply, and disturbance from boats.

# The Galápagos Islands

**Important area**
This region is so important that both the islands and the sea around them have been declared a World Heritage Site to protect them from harm.

The Galápagos Islands are a group of volcanic islands that lie 560 miles (900 km) off the coast of Ecuador, straddling the equator. These islands were made famous when Charles Darwin visited them in 1835. There he discovered a unique group of plants and animals that set off a train of ideas that led to his theory of evolution. He believed that the animals and plants had evolved from ancestors that were carried to the islands either by wind or water from the mainland. There they adapted to the conditions on the different islands. For example, the ancestral finch that arrived from the mainland has developed into approximately 12 different species, each found on a different island and feeding on a different range of foods.

## MARINE IGUANAS

Although the different populations of marine iguanas (*Amblyrhynchus cristatus*) vary in size and color, they are all the same species. Most are a sooty black, sometimes with patches of green or red. They feed on seaweed in the shallow waters around the islands. Iguanas are ectothermic animals, meaning that their body temperature is the same as their surroundings. As they swim in cold water, their bodies cool down, so they clamber onto the rocks to bask in the sun and warm up. These iguanas are only found in the Galápagos Islands, and they are very sensitive to both changes in their environment, such as a shortage of food, and to pollution, such as an oil spill.

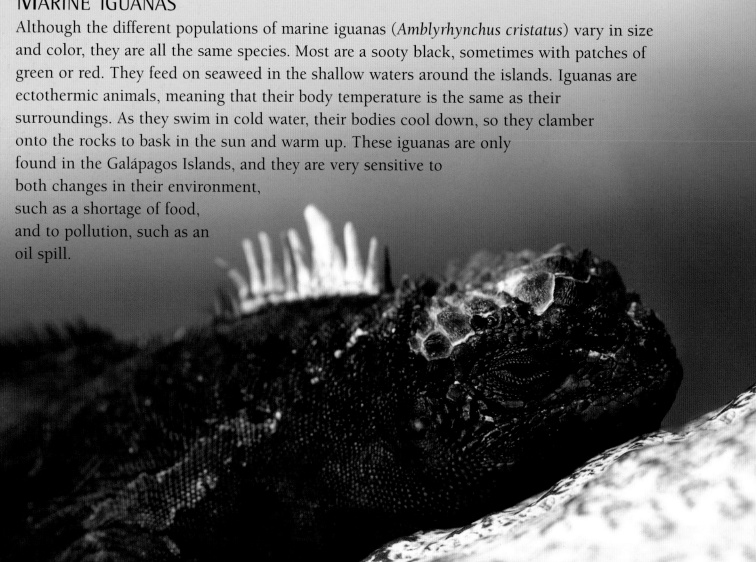

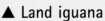

# CONSERVING THE ISLANDS

The Galápagos is the world's largest oceanic archipelago (group of islands) with its biodiversity nearly intact. In recent years, there have been a lot of problems facing the islands, both political and environmental. There are two key issues. The first is the introduction of species such as goats, pigs, cats, dogs, rats, and plants that have arrived with people. The goats and pigs have overgrazed the vegetation, while the rats and cats prey on indigenous species. There are now programs to control these introduced species. The waters around the islands are rich in fish, attracting fishermen. There are fishing zones and quota systems in place, but the fishermen are not happy with the arrangements, and there has been conflict between them and the authorities. A lot of illegal fishing still takes place, threatening the survival of many species.

## ▲ Land iguana

There are two species of land iguana found in the Galápagos Islands, *Conolophus subcristatus* and *Conolophus pallidus*. These yellow iguanas are more than 3.3 ft (1 m) long and weigh up to 29 lbs (13 kg). They live in the drier areas of the islands where they feed mainly on low-growing plants, such as the cactus. Hunting by wild dogs is threatening this species. In 1976, wild dogs killed about 500 land iguanas on Santa Cruz Island, and in the following years, more iguanas were killed on other islands. To help re-establish the land iguana populations, the wild dogs have been removed from several islands, and a breeding program has been established so that individuals can be reintroduced to the wild.

## ◀ Galápagos giant tortoise

Galápagos giant tortoises (*Geochelone elephantopus*) can weigh up to 550 lbs (250 kg) and live for more than 100 years. They are thought to belong to just one species, with 14 different sub-species, three of which are believed to be extinct. There is a great variety of shell shapes. Originally there may have been 100,000 tortoises, but many have been killed for their meat, and now fewer than 15,000 survive, mostly in the highland areas.

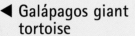

## ▲ Charles mockingbird

There are four species of Galápagos mockingbird, including the endangered Charles mockingbird (*Nesomimus trifasciatus*). Only the Charles mockingbird is found on more than one island. The mockingbirds are unafraid of people and are very curious. They will explore any unknown object, looking for food or drink.

## ▶ Galápagos penguin

The Galápagos penguin (*Spheniscus mendiculus*) is the most northerly occurring of all the penguin species. To keep cool in the tropical heat, they hold their flippers out to help the heat escape from their bodies. During much of the day, they swim and hunt for food in the cold water, and then come ashore at night to sleep. Galápagos penguins eat mostly small fish, such as mullet and sardines. They are dependent on the ocean currents to bring fish to their feeding grounds. During the 1980s, they suffered a shortage of food, and 70 percent of the penguins died. Since then their numbers have increased to 800 breeding pairs, but they are still listed as endangered.

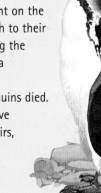

## ▶ Flightless cormorant

The flightless cormorant (*Compsohalieus harrisi*) can only be found in the Galápagos Islands and is the only cormorant that cannot fly. These are the heaviest members of the cormorant family, and they feed on octopus. Originally there were no natural predators for the cormorant on the islands, but this changed when people introduced dogs and cats. There are now only about 1,000 flightless cormorants, and the species is listed as rare.

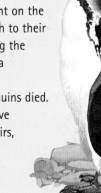

# New Zealand

New Zealand was cut off from the rest of the world for 90 million years. As a result, it is a place where a high percentage of its species are found only there, in New Zealand. It is inhabited by birds and reptiles. With just two species of mammals (bats), animals did not develop defense mechanisms to fight or escape from mammal predators. Then, about a thousand years ago, the first people landed and started to clear the forests. They brought a species of rat, "*kiore*," as well as other mammals. Europeans arrived in the 1800s and brought their pets and livestock.

## Island conflict

Mammalian predators such as cats, dogs, and rats found it easy to prey on native animals such as kiwis, kakapos, and takahes. Many New Zealand animals became extinct, including the moa (a large flightless bird), while about 1,000 other species are currently at risk.

## KAKAPO

The flightless kakapo (*Strigops habroptilus*) is the world's rarest parrot. It the also the world's only flightless and nocturnal parrot, as well as the heaviest parrot, at 8 lbs (3.5 kg). This parrot was once common throughout the three main islands of New Zealand. Their decline started when the first Polynesian people arrived and hunted the kakapo for its skin and feathers, clearing the forests in which they lived. The Europeans killed the birds for their meat, and then they were hunted by introduced cats and stoats. The kakapo population fell from hundreds of thousands to just 51. These remaining birds have been relocated to six predator-free island habitats, where they are relatively safe. Their numbers have crept up to 86.

# CONSERVING UNIQUE SPECIES

New Zealand's wildlife is threatened by the destruction of habitats and by introduced predators and weeds. There are a number of conservation programs aimed at protecting New Zealand's unique wildlife. Many nature reserves have been established to protect the most valuable wildlife habitats, such as Trounson Kauri Park, where there are brown kiwi, short-eared bats, and rare snails; and Tiritiri Matangi Island, which has been replanted with forest and is predator-free. Several other island sanctuaries are now free of introduced predators and have had revegetation projects to restore habitats. Many endangered birds and reptiles have been transferred to these islands. Mainland sanctuaries are being set up and monitored so that threatened native species can flourish.

## ▶ Kiwi

The kiwi is a flightless bird that is unique to New Zealand. There are six species of kiwi (*Apteryx sp.*), of which the brown kiwi is the most widespread and numerous. Some survive only on islands. The decline of the kiwi is a result of habitat loss and the introduction of predators. Young kiwis, which leave the nest at three weeks of age, are most at risk, as they only weigh 7 oz (200 g) and are easy prey. The Kiwi Recovery Program, launched in 1991, aims to maintain as many species as possible, to increase the number of kiwi, and to increase the number of places in which they can live.

## ◀ Hochstetter's frog

Hochstetter's frog (*Lejopelma hochstetteri*) is found in the North Island. It grows to up to 1.8 in (4.5 cm) in length and has partially webbed feet. It lives along the edges of streams. Its population has declined as a result of land development, habitat destruction, and hunting by mammals, especially the Norway rat. Although it is one of the most widespread of New Zealand's seven native species of frog, it is found in only a fraction of its former range.

## ◀ Tuatara

The tuatara (*Sphenodon punctatum*) is an ancient reptile that looks like a lizard. These long-lived reptiles do not breed until they reach the age of about 15, and then the females lay eggs only every three or four years. Once they were found throughout New Zealand, but now they survive only on 32 offshore islands. These islands are free of rodents and other introduced predators that eat the eggs and young of the tuatara.

## ▶ New Zealand short-tailed bat

Most bats catch their prey in the air, but the short-tailed bat is adapted to ground hunting. It spends long periods of time on the forest floor using its folded wings as front "limbs" for scrambling around as it searches for insects, fruit, and pollen. There are two species of short-tailed bat. The greater short-tailed bat (*Mystacina robusta*) was last sighted in 1967 and is probably extinct. The endangered lesser short-tailed bat (*Mystacina tuberculata*) is found at only a few scattered sites.

## ▶ Takahe

The takahe (*Notornis mantelli*) is a bird about the size of a large hen, covered in blue and green feathers. It has small wings, but they are not used for flying. The takahe once lived throughout New Zealand, but it was hunted by the Maoris, and numbers fell. The birds retreated to the remote Murchison Mountains, where they were safe from the hunters. However, they were then threatened by the introduction of deer that competed with the takahe for tussock grasses. New populations of this bird have been established on predator-free islands, where they are thriving.

## ▶ Wrybill

The wrybill (*Anarhynchus frontalis*) lives on the coast. It has a very distinctive beak, which curves to the right. It feeds by probing under stones and by sweeping its beak through shallow, muddy water to find small animals. It breeds on gravel river banks. Wrybills are listed as threatened due to habitat loss, disturbance, and introduced mammals.

# Glossary

ANTARCTIC The region of the world that lies around the South Pole and extends up to the Antarctic Circle

ARCTIC The region of the world that lies around the North Pole and extends down to the Arctic Circle

AMPHIBIAN A kind of animal that is cold-blooded and lays its eggs in water. Adult amphibians breathe air, while infant amphibians, or larvae, take oxygen from water by using gills. Amphibians include frogs, toads, and salamanders.

ARABLE FARMING Growing crops by plowing the soil

ARID Extremely dry and barren

ATOLL A ring formed by a coral reef that surrounds a shallow pool, called a lagoon

BIODIVERSITY The range of different plant and animal species in an environment

BRACKISH Water that is slightly salty

CLOUD FOREST Also called montane rain forest, this is a kind of forest that lies high up on mountain slopes in tropical parts of the world. Clouds surround these forests all year because of the cooling effect of the high altitude.

CONIFEROUS A tree or shrub, such as a pine or fur, that bears cones and usually remains green all winter

CONSERVATION The preservation or protection of something, such as a species or a region and ecosystem

DECIDUOUS A tree or bush that drops its leaves each fall

DEFORESTATION The cutting down of large areas of forests and woodlands in order to clear land for farming and mining or to use the wood from the trees

DINOSAUR A kind of animal that first appeared about 200 million years ago. These reptiles developed into many different species and dominated life on the land until they became extinct 65 million years ago.

ENDANGERED When the numbers of an animal or a plant have become so low that they face extinction

EQUATOR An invisible line of latitude that runs around the earth at its widest point. Regions around the equator are usually the hottest places on the planet.

ESTUARY The mouth of a river and the point where it flows into the sea

EXTINCT When an animal or plant ceases to exist

FLOODPLAIN A flat area around a river that is regularly flooded

HERBIVORES Animals that only eat plants

LAGOON A shallow area of water that has been blocked off from a larger body of water, such as the sea

MAMMAL A kind of animal that is warm-blooded, produces milk to feed its young, and has hair on some or all of its body. Mammals include horses, rats, gorillas, whales, and humans.

MARSUPIAL A kind of mammal that bears young that complete their development in a pouch on the mother's belly. Marsupials include kangaroos and wallabies.

MIGRATION Movement from one region to another at particular times of year. For example, many birds fly south in the winter.

OVERFISHING To take too many fish out of the water. This means that the fish cannot replace their numbers quickly enough, and the numbers of fish decline.

PESTICIDE A mix of chemicals that destroys unwanted plants or animals

PRAIRIE An area of grassland found in North America

PREDATOR An animal that hunts another animal

RAIN FOREST A forested area, usually found in tropical parts of the world, that has at least 100 in (254 cm) of rainfall every year. The leaves of the trees form a continuous layer, called the canopy.

REEF A strip of rocks, sand, or coral that lies near the surface of the water and close to the coast of an island or the mainland. Coral reefs are formed from the skeletons of millions of tiny creatures called coral polyps.

RUMINANT A kind of mammal that has a four-chambered stomach. Ruminants are plant-eaters. They can bring up, or regurgitate, food they have already eaten, in order to chew it again and release more nutrients.

SAVANNAH A type of grassland found in Africa where few trees grow

SILT Small particles of mud and rock that are carried along by streams and rivers

STEPPE A large area of grassland found in southeastern Europe and Asia

TAIGA A region of forest that lies to the south of the tundra. These forests are formed mainly of conifers.

TEMPERATE REGIONS Parts of the world that lie to the north and south of the tropics. These regions are cooler than the tropics and extend to the polar regions at the top and bottom of the world.

TROPICS Parts of the world that lie on either side of the Equator, up to the Tropic of Cancer to the north and the Tropic of Capricorn to the south

TUNDRA A treeless region found to the south of the Arctic Circle where the ground just beneath the surface remains frozen solid all year round

WETLANDS A region that has a large amount of water. Wetlands include swamps, marshes, rivers, and lakes.

## Conservation Organizations

### World Conservation Union

The World Conservation Union is also known as the IUCN (International Union for the Conservation of Nature and Natural Resources). This organization was founded in October 1948, and it is the world's largest and most important conservation network. It is probably best known for its work in monitoring the state of the world's species through the IUCN *Red List of Threatened Species*. Its aim is to influence, encourage, and assist governments and organizations throughout the world to conserve nature and to ensure that any use of natural resources is ecologically sustainable.

*www.iucn.org*

### WWF

WWF (Worldwide Fund for Nature) was launched in the United Kingdom in 1961 and has grown into the world's largest and most experienced independent conservation organization. It has 5 million supporters around the world and carries out projects in more than 90 countries. The work of the WWF involves active conservation in threatened habitats, creation of protected areas, educating people, advising governments, and campaigning on issues such as climate change and sustainability.

*www.wwf.org* and *www.panda.org*

### Greenpeace International

Greenpeace was founded in 1971 when a small boat of volunteers and journalists sailed into Amchitka, an area north of Alaska where the United States government was conducting underground nuclear tests. Their aim was to stop the tests in a nonviolent way. Today Greenpeace works in 40 countries in Europe, the Americas, Asia, and the Pacific. It has 2.8 million supporters. To maintain its independence, Greenpeace does not accept donations from governments or corporations, but relies on contributions from individual supporters. Greenpeace focuses on the most important threats to biodiversity and the environment, such as climate change, deforestation, pollution of the oceans, whaling, nuclear testing, genetic engineering, and toxic wastes. Greenpeace also encourages sustainable trade.

*www.greenpeace.org/international*

### The Sierra Club

The Sierra Club was formed in 1892 and is the United States' oldest and largest environmental organization, with 750,000 members. One of its first actions was to lead the campaign to prevent the reduction in the size of Yosemite National Park. Today it works to protect the environment and conserve wilderness areas. Most recently, the organization has been campaigning to protect some of the country's forests.

*www.sierraclub.org*

# Index

# Acknowledgments

**Photographic credits**

t=top; b=bottom; l=left; r=right

Front cover left—Dreamstime.com, Phil Date, center—Dreamstime.com, Mike Carlson, right—Dreamstime.com, Hilary Bell, Back cover—Dreamstime.com

3—istockphoto.com, 6-7, 6b—Digital Vision, 7t—Dreamstime.com, Wang Sanjun, 8-9—Dreamstime.com, 9b—Digital Vision, 10b—Alamy/DigiPro Photography & Imaging, 11t—istockphoto.com, 11b—Dreamstime.com, 12—istockphoto.com, 14—Dreamstime.com, Anthony Hathaway, 16—istockphoto.com, 18—istockphoto.com, 20-21—Tall Tree Ltd., 21b—Digital Vision, 22b—Digital Vision, 23t—Dreamstime.com, Mairead Neal, 23b—Ardea/Kenneth W. Fink, 24—Dreamstime.com, Ethan Kocak, 26—Dreamstime.com, Tim Goodwin, 28—Dreamstime.com, Phil Date, 30-31—Dreamstime.com, Christopher Davies, 31b—Dreamstime.com, Joe Gough, 32b—Ardea/Kenneth W. Fink, 33t—istockphoto.com, 33b—Dreamstime.com, Yegor Korzh, 34—Dreamstime.com, Hilary Bell, 36—Dreamstime.com, Jostein Hauge, 38—Dreamstime.com, Graça Victoria, 40-41—Dreamstime.com, Steffen Foerster, 41b—Dreamstime.com, Wang Sanjun, 42b—Dreamstime.com, Jerry Dupree, 43t—Dreamstime.com, Steffen Foerster, 43b—istockphoto.com, 44—Dreamstime.com, Phil Date, 46—Corbis/Theo Allofs, 48—Corbis/Martin Harvey/Gallo Images, 50-51—Dreamstime.com, Sergey Poluyan, 51b—courtesy of John Deere, 52b—Ardea/Pat Leeson, 53t—Ardea/Kenneth W. Fink, 53b—Ardea/Nick Gordon, 54—Alamy/Juniors Bildarchiv, 56—Ardea/Jagdeep Rajput, 58-59—Dreamstime.com, Wilmy Van Ulft, 59b—istockphoto.com, 60b—Dreamstime.com, 61t—Alamy/Holt Studios International Ltd, 61b—Ardea/Kenneth W. Fink, 62—Alamy/Bruce Coleman INC., 64—Alamy/Elvele Images, 66-67—Digital Vision, 67b—Corbis/Galen Rowell, 68b—Ardea/Kenneth W. Fink, 69t—Dreamstime.com, Sergey Anatolievich, 69b—Dreamstime.com, Graça Victoria, 70—Corbis/Roger Tidman, 72—Ardea/Joanna Van Gruisen, 74—Dreamstime.com, Mike Carlson, 76-77—Digital Vision, 77b—Digital Vision, 78—Corbis/Ralph White, 79t—istockphoto.com, 79b—Dreamstime.com, 80—Getty Images, 82—Dreamstime.com, Lau Choon Siew, 84—Corbis/W. Perry Conway, 86—Dreamstim.com, Craig Ruaux, 88—Ardea/Auscape

**Artwork credits**

Alan Male, Andrew Robinson, Barry Croucher/Wildlife Art Agency, Brian Delf, Chris Orr Associates, Chris Rose, Christian Webb/Temple Rogers, David Quinn, Denys Ovenden, Dianne Breeze, Chris Christoforou, Dick Twinney, Eric Robson, Gill Tomblin, Graham Allen/Wildlife Art Agency, Ian Jackson/Wildlife Art Agency, John Francis, Ken Wood, Malcom Ellis, Michael Woods, Norman Arlott, Owen Williams, Peter David Scott/Wildlife Art Agency, Peter Hayman, Richard Bonson, Robert Gilmour, Robin Boutell/Wildlife Art Agency, Russell Barnett, Sandra Doyle/Wildlife Art Agency, Steve Kirk, Tudor Humphries